Therezinha

One Lighthouse Press

Therezinha
By Kevin Allen

TO CAROL CLASCO

BEST WISHES,

Kev

Published by One Lighthouse Press
22 Dutton Court, Marin City, CA 94965

Second Printing 2000

ISBN 0-9671490-0-2

Printed in the United States of America

"Library of Congress Catalog card number" 99-70480

For more information, write One Lighthouse Press
22 Dutton Court, Marin City, CA 94965

Cover design and layout by Donohue Design Co.
info@donohuedesign.com
www.donohuedesign.com

Dedication

This book is dedicated to the memory of my grandfather, Lincoln Dunbar Simpson, who, with an open heart, gave me so much wisdom and guidance. Even though he has passed, I felt his support throughout this writing.

Chapter
One

The first plans for a trip to Brazil came about in 1987, when Kenneth and I returned to San Francisco from Mardi Gras in New Orleans. The trip, our first time traveling together, went very well, and my childhood buddy and I talked about another vacation. Kenneth and I did fight and argue with one another at the beginning of the trip—we hadn't traveled together before or spent that much time together since the old days, when we would spend the night at each other's house as school kids. So, we had to get over our differences as adults the best way we could without ruining Mardi Gras. New Orleans was wild, the music was great, and the food was excellent. We both enjoyed walking up and down Bourbon Street, looking at the women. Kenneth left two days before me. It was planned that way. But by then we had both decided that the following year we would travel together to Rio de Janeiro, Brazil, and would make definite plans when we were both back in San Francisco. We had heard that the Carnival in Brazil was the best in the world and that the women were the finest. The idea of a trip out of the country was very exciting to me and gave me something to look forward to in the following year.

Later that same year, in early August, I went to Fort Lauderdale, Florida, to visit family. My Uncle E.J. married a woman from the Dominican Republic, Carmen. Aunt Carmen is beautiful. Perhaps because of time spent with Uncle E.J. and Aunt Carmen, I began to think of marrying a woman from another country, such as the Caribbean. While visiting in Fort Lauderdale, I decided to take a short trip to the Dominican Republic. It was less than two hours by plane from Miami, and since I had my passport with me, I thought I might as well use it. That was the reason why I applied for it in the first place—to travel the world.

I was a little nervous about traveling out of the country by myself for the first time. I didn't speak Spanish, the language of the Dominican Republic, but the trip was something that I had to experience by myself. My uncle gave me phone numbers of Aunt Carmen's family and told me to call them.

When I arrived, I met Aunt Carmen's brother, Carlos, and his wife. They were very good to me. I spent the days by myself, just walking around the town. The women of the Dominican Republic were exotic and very beautiful. They had pretty brown skin and silky hair and gentle, open smiles. I had never seen women like that before. I had taken many pictures so that I could show my friends in San Francisco. The women in the Dominican Republic were quite *bonita*, which means beautiful, and after that short trip, I couldn't wait to go to Rio de Janeiro.

Chapter
Two

In February 1988, Kenneth and I left San Francisco for Brazil. We flew to Miami and then from there to Rio de Janeiro. Once in Miami, we boarded a second plane, and the flight attendant said the flight would take eight hours. I had never been on a plane for that long, and I remember thinking to myself, 'Wow, a whole work day up in an airplane with nothing to do. How boring a trip this is going to be!' By the time we left Miami, it was night and it began to storm. The plane was shaking as we took off. I looked at Kenneth and he looked back and I could tell he was scared. I was scared too. I wondered if this trip was such a good idea after all. By the time we had reached 35,000 feet, the air calmed down and the plane seemed to cruise. The noise and the shaking stopped. One of the flight attendants gave us a meal, and we saw two movies. Then I went to sleep. Before long, the sun was shining through the plane's windows and the captain said that we were about an hour from Galiao International Airport. That was good news and I was happy about landing. The eight-hour flight went by really fast! Before I knew it, the plane was landing. Both Kenneth and I were excited, and we hurried out of the plane.

We passed through Customs, got our baggage and proceeded out of the airport. In an instant, I saw Kenneth talking to a lady at the tourist booth. He had bought some maps and brochures. I told him that we would probably get the same materials from the tour guide.

"You're right, but she was so beautiful—I had to buy them."

I laughed and said, "Okay."

We were waiting to be met by a person from the tour company. After that we would be taken to our hotel. We waited and waited, but no one greeted us. We went outside to catch a taxi. It was hot. February is summer time in Rio. The language in Brazil is Portuguese, and neither of us spoke a word of Portuguese. Finally, we got a cab and headed for Copacabana Beach. The name of our hotel was Hotel California. How fitting, considering we were both from California. When we arrived, we checked in and called the tour company. We complained about not being met at the airport and having to pay more than fifty *cruseros* for the taxi. They apologized, but that was all they did.

We settled in our room. It was a small room with two beds in the back of the hotel. We had no view of the beach. Kenneth was upset about that because he thought the room would have a view of the beach. It didn't matter much to me. I was just happy to be there.

After lunch we went outside. There were streams of people walking down Copacabana Beach, and most of the women on the beach were wearing string bikinis. It was an unbelievable sight! We walked past a lot of sidewalk cafes filled with *cariocas*, natives of Brazil, and tourists alike. Everyone drank beer, soda, water, whatever your taste, and just watched the women pass by. There were lots of children on the streets of Rio, most of them obviously homeless. They came up to us and begged for money. Kenneth and I gave them a few dollars. It seemed like the right thing to do… We walked around a little too, familiarizing ourselves with the area, window-shopping and taking in all of the sights. We walked down the beach front in the torrid heat, and after awhile, we had to return to our room to rest. Jet lag was catching up with us.

It was now Thursday; it had taken us a day to travel to Rio. Rio time is six hours ahead of Pacific Standard Time, and my body was trying to adjust to the time difference. After resting for a few hours, we decided to have dinner. We found a little restaurant not too far from our hotel, and we were still on Copacabana Beach. The restaurant was crowded, but we didn't have to wait too long for a table. The food was good—steak and lobster—if I remember correctly. After dinner we walked back toward our hotel. Night life in Rio starts around 11:00PM. We sat outside our hotel and watched the people walk back and forth. A man came out of the hotel and sat down next to us. We began talking. He spoke English, which was good to hear by that time. He said his name was Gus. Gus talked with an accent I couldn't detect. He wasn't from the United States, he told us. He had been to Rio many times for Carnival, and he assured us that we were about to have a very exciting and enjoyable time. And we were sure that Gus was right. We could feel the excitement in the air.

Gus told us about a ball being held at Monte Libano. Libano is a town located on the other side of Ipanema Beach, not far from Copacabana Beach, only ten minutes by taxi. We had paid our tour company to get tickets for us for the different Carnival balls and Samba parades, but we didn't have a ticket for the Monte Libano Ball. After talking more with Gus, Kenneth and I decided that we would go the next day and buy tickets for that ball. According to Gus, it was the one event not to be missed.

After about an hour, Gus left. One thing about Gus was that he would talk about anything and everything. He enjoyed telling us about Rio de Janeiro, since he had visited so many times. After Gus left, Kenneth and I decided to get dressed and go out on the town. We wouldn't venture too far the first night; we'd just walk up and down Copacabana and check out some discos. It was around 10:30 PM when we left the hotel. We walked around, looked at the partying crowds and checked out the local scene. There was a lot going on both inside and outside of the sidewalk cafes, and lots and lots of women were hanging around at every turn. We also noticed that there were huge crowds of tourists at Copacabana Beach. Since it was Carnival time, it was time to party.

We went into a disco club and were surprised by the loud and jamming music. It was a fairly large disco with a balcony circling the dance floor. From both sides of the floor you could walk upstairs, along the balcony and then downstairs. The place was filled with tourists and beautiful bronze women of all different shapes and sizes dressed in every color of the rainbow. We stayed for about an hour and a half, listening to the Brazilian and American music, and, of course, looking at the beautiful women moving on and off the dance floor and between the tables. We decided to go back to the hotel before too long. We had planned to go on a tour of Corcovado Mountain the next day. This is the world-famous mountain that displays the statue of Christ the Redeemer.

The next morning we got up early. The hotel served a breakfast that was excellent—fresh fruit, all kinds of juices, bacon and eggs, and pastries. It was the best meal of the day for me. After breakfast, we went to the front of the hotel to meet the bus. It was due at 8:30AM and it was close to 9:00AM when we thought to ourselves, 'Here we go again…'

About a half hour later the bus pulled up front and a lady came into the hotel lobby. She introduced herself as Toni and said, "The bus is waiting."

We left the hotel and boarded the bus. The bus was about half full, and Kenneth and I had plenty of good seats to choose from. As the bus slowly started to climb the nearby hills, the tour guide began to point out the homes of some Brazilian movie stars and famous actors in one particular suburb. We passed some really huge estates. About a half hour later the bus stopped, and the tour left the bus. We then had to board a train that would take us up the side of Corcovado Mountain. It was as if a roller-coaster was taking us through the jungle. The air was cool, fresh and clean. About ten minutes later we were at the top of Corcovado Mountain, and in front of us was the enormous statue of Christ. It was really amazing to see this. According to the tour guide, it took the workers five years of construction to build the statue on its mountain site. Christ's arms are stretched out over the city of Rio de Janeiro. The day was cloudy, so the view wasn't as good as it would have been on a clear day, but Kenneth and I could still see the beautiful beaches below and the many hotels that encompassed the area.

We took pictures of the statue and then returned to the train taking us back to the bus. On the way down the mountain, the bus stopped so we could take pictures of Maracana, the world's biggest soccer stadium, which had been built specifically for the 1950 World Cup Games. The stadium holds over 100,000 people. We viewed the stadium from its top, so we could see right down inside the structure. Sure was big! The grass of the playing field was an even, bright green—they keep it well maintained. After that we headed back to the hotel. The next day we planned on touring Sugarloaf Mountain.

It was about 2:00PM when we got back to the hotel. Kenneth and I were both hungry, so we went out for lunch. At one of the sidewalk cafes, we ordered some food. As we ate and watched the scenes around us, each of which had filled with more and more people. It was now Friday and Carnival was about to begin that night. A girl walked by our table, and she looked at Kenneth. She had a good-looking body, and she stood out in the crowd. Her face was pretty and she wore braces. Kenneth noticed her. She walked over to us. She could speak a little English. Her name was Angela and she stayed in Copacabana. She talked while we ate lunch. After lunch, she and Kenneth decided to walk around. I didn't want to tag along, so I went for a walk on the beach. There weren't many *cariocas* at the beach, but there were still some nice sights in bikinis. After awhile, I returned to the hotel.

About two hours later, Kenneth returned from his walk with Angela, and he seemed happy. Kenneth never had any problems with women. Women always seemed to be attracted to him. He said that Angela had a friend, and she would bring her next time to meet me.

"Great, then we both can go walking," I replied.

Nightfall came upon us pretty fast. We were waiting to go to a nightclub called Scalla for the Red and Black Ball. We had heard that this ball was supposed to be one of the better Carnival balls, maybe one of the best. When we got dressed, we made sure that we wore something either red or black so that we would blend in with the crowd. The Red and Black Ball is sponsored every year by the Flamingo Soccer Team in Brazil. It is a famous soccer team that has won a lot of the championships for Brazil.

About 11:00PM we left the hotel by taxi to the Scalla nightclub. The taxi ride was about fifteen minutes. When we arrived in front of this huge nightclub, there was a line of people waiting to get in the club. Also there were mobs of people in the street just hanging out, looking to see who was going in and who was coming out. It was an unbelievable sight, seeing all of the *cariocas* as we stood in line to enter the club. Finally, the line moved and we headed for the entrance. We could only imagine what was going on inside. When we were at the door, we gave the man our tickets and he let us in the club. Wow! It was packed with young, exotic women walking around topless and dancing to a twenty-piece band that was blasting music throughout the nightclub. The band never stopped playing. The musicians played continuously, taking shifts, rotating from one musician to another without stopping. Being in the nightclub made us feel as if we were in an exotic frenzy, the kind of feeling that one would actually have to experience to understand. The place was 'going on!' I walked around the bottom floor which was packed with people, all doing their 'thing.' The music was crystal clear with a Brazilian beat that sounded really good.

The club had an upstairs balcony. I didn't walk up the stairs to the balcony. Instead, I looked up and saw nothing but beautiful women dancing and showing off their breasts. I couldn't believe it! Then it hit me, "This is Rio de Janeiro, Brazil, and it is happening!"

Kenneth was as excited as I was. We didn't talk; we just looked in amazement at everything. The place was packed. No one could move without bumping into someone else. Of course, no man would mind saying, "*Desculpe*," if he had bumped into one of the beautiful girls trying to move around the tables or onto the dance floor. Women with full body paint were dancing on top of tables. The women of Brazil are simply beautiful, their smiles, their faces, all with different kinds of silky hair. I must admit, girls with silky hair turn me on.

Suddenly I noticed a friend of mine walking through the crowd. I wasn't sure it was possible that I would meet someone that I knew in Brazil, but after a little bumping and pushing I caught up with him. It was my friend Michael! We had worked together about eight years ago driving school buses. What a small world! Michael couldn't believe what he was seeing at the ball either, but he was sure enough enjoying the scenery. Michael had come to Rio with another tour company whose hotel was on the northeast side of Brazil. And they arrived for Carnival just in time, according to Michael. After talking with my old buddy for awhile, we finally said, "Later."

I began to walk the floor. There was a lot of drinking going on inside the Scalla. One guy passed out in front of me. He looked almost dead; it was a bad sight. The heat was incredible inside the nightclub; it was almost like being in an oven that was turned on to "broil." But I had no complaints because I was caught up in the atmosphere of the whole situation. Eventually I bumped back into Kenneth, and we walked around the place. The women in there were friendly, always smiling. Of course, we couldn't say much to them because we couldn't speak Portuguese, and most of them couldn't speak English. That was the only problem. I couldn't talk to any of them, just look at them, and stare as if they were statues. But they didn't mind, because everyone was having a great time. Considering how crowded the place was, everyone seemed to get along very well.

Still, I kept my eye on the exit sign just in case of trouble; I had no idea what was going on outside of my view. It was now about 3:00AM, and the band was still playing, and people were still dancing. From the time I walked into the nightclub, there was no place to sit down. And now I was ready to go back to the hotel. Kenneth was ready also, so we went outside to get a taxi.

Many people were outside, as many as when we first arrived, and now they were watching people come out.

'Wow, Rio is something!' I thought.

We found a taxi and headed back to Copacabana Beach. When we got back, we went to bed.

"What a night!"

Kenneth yelled back, "You can say that again!"

Then I said, "Good night."

The morning arrived really fast. I woke about 9:00AM. I asked Kenneth, "What about the tour to Sugarloaf? The bus will be here at 9:30AM."

Kenneth mumbled, "We'll go tomorrow."

"Fine. I'm tired anyway."

Later, we got up and went down to the hotel lobby for breakfast. Breakfast was the best thing about this hotel. Everything else was just so-so.

After breakfast we decided to sit in front of the hotel. We noticed a guy with a bunch of children. They stopped in front of the hotel. His said his name was Julius. He lived in the *favela* just behind Copacabana. He was a tall, slim man with gray-black hair. He spoke a little English, so we began to talk with him and the children. The morning was a sunny Saturday and the beaches were filling up with *cariocas* and tourists alike. After a few minutes, Julius, the kids, Kenneth and I decided to walk around a little and look in the stores. I saw some nice clothes and shoes. Brazilians make nice bright shirts that stand out and have a very classy look. I saw a flamingo sweatsuit with the red and black colors, and after last night's party, I wanted it. I liked the colors and from that point on, I became a Flamingo team fan. In Brazil, they call soccer "football" because they use their feet when playing. Everybody loves soccer in Brazil, and they should. Brazilians are the best players in the world. But, of course, everybody knows that.

After shopping for about an hour, we decided to go back to the hotel. Kenneth reminded me that Angela would be coming around 1:00PM, so he wanted to make sure that he was back. We stayed outside the hotel and sat in front of the tables. Angela and her friend passed by and came to our table. She introduced her friend to me. She was tall and slim, and she wasn't my type anyway. We left to find a place to have lunch, preferably at an outside cafe. We ordered lunch, and Kenneth and Angela talked. Even though Angela could speak a little English, her friend, my lunch date, could not. Angela and Kenneth made plans to meet one another later that day. Then I heard someone call my name. I looked up, and it was my friend Michael. He was out walking and noticed our table. He sat down, and we talked for awhile; afterwards, Michael continued down Copacabana Beach.

After lunch we walked around some more. When Angela and her friend left, Kenneth and I walked back to the hotel. We discussed plans for the evening. It was mid-afternoon, and we remembered that we needed to get tickets to the Monte Libano Ball. We caught a taxi to Leblon and stood in line for tickets.

Before we knew it, nightfall was upon us again. We got dressed and went out. Again, the Copacabana beach front was crowded with people. Carnival time! You could sense the excitement in the air. The sky was clouding up, and it looked as if it would shower at any minute. We knew it was a tropical country, where the rain stops after one or two short downpours. People tend to take cover and then return after the shower. We went to a club, and it was packed again with beautiful women, all, of course, topless and dancing. I thought I had seen it all, but I hadn't.

We found a table upstairs where we could look out onto the floor and see the action around us. We saw an African American guy and an American standing along the balcony, looking over at the crowd.

"Those guys were on the plane with us when we flew down here from San Francisco," I said.

"For real?"

I went up to the African American guy and said, "Hi, my name is Kevin." And we began talking.

Both were from San Francisco, just like us. I invited them over to our table, and we began to talk and check out the scene together. It was a frenzied atmosphere again with lots of Brazilian girls walking around, shaking their butts and dancing. It was a sight to see! The African American guy told us his name was Sage and his friend's name was Johnny. They drank and really enjoyed themselves. Kenneth and I don't drink, so we sat back and watched and laughed at everybody. We enjoyed doing that.

A woman came over to us, climbed up on the table and started dancing and stripping. Wow! I just sat there, totally shocked at what was happening. There were all kinds of women walking around the club, and downstairs we could see that the club was totally packed to the walls. This partying went on for hours. About 2:00AM, I was ready to go. Well, not exactly ready, but I knew that we should leave if we were going to go on the tour to Sugarloaf the next morning. We said goodbye to our friends and left.

The next morning, about 8:00AM, I called the tour company and told them that we wanted to go on the tour. The guide said the bus would be at our hotel at 1:00PM. I fell back to sleep. About three hours later, I woke up. Kenneth was not in the room. I got dressed and went down to the lobby. Kenneth was sitting outside the hotel, girl-watching. Angela came by. She said that she had waited for Kenneth by the hotel last night until about 2:00AM. She was by herself this time. Some kids interrupted us, asking for money. I gave them some, and they left. Then Gus happened to walk by, and he came over to our table and said hello. He asked if we bought tickets to Monte Libano, and I told him yes. He assured us that it would be a good ball. I said, "We'll see."

It was getting close to 1:00PM, and I reminded Kenneth that the bus would be coming shortly. Angela left, and soon the tour bus came. The tour guide, Chocolate, told us that he spoke twenty-seven languages. I couldn't comprehend how someone could speak that many different tongues.

It was a clear afternoon that Sunday, and we went to Sugarloaf Mountain. Visitors have to take a cable tram to the top of the mountain, and it's an adventure for anybody. Once at the top of Sugarloaf Mountain, you can see all of Rio. It was a beautiful sight to see. Somehow, Kenneth and I got separated from the group, but on the way down the mountain, Kenneth spotted Chocolate and the group farther ahead, loading into the bus.

Kenneth said, "I'll catch them and have them wait for you."

We returned to our hotel about 5:00PM after touring around town looking at different points of interest. We were hungry and went to a restaurant to eat and talk about how things were going. For both of us, this trip was much better than the New Orleans trip. We seemed to have gotten along great and were having more fun. Of course, with beautiful women all around, who wouldn't enjoy it? For both of us, though, the language barrier was tough to get around. But we did try to pick up some words in Portuguese, so that we could try to communicate.

After dinner we headed back to the hotel. I was tired from the parties of the two previous nights, and we had no ball tickets for that evening. We sat out front of the hotel for awhile, looking at the beach and the people walking by. Eventually I went to the room to watch TV and relax. Locations of Carnival balls were being broadcast throughout the whole city, so no one in town was missing anything. My mind drifted back to San Francisco. I had been in business at the time for three years as a school bus contractor. And I was planning to expand my business and get more contracts. I wanted the time to think and reflect on what I had accomplished so far and where I wanted to go. It was a good feeling to relax in this setting. Still, romance was on my mind too, but I hadn't seen anyone I could talk to or get to know. So what. I was going to just enjoy myself and not worry about anything. I went to bed early that night.

Morning came. I got up early and went to get breakfast by myself. After awhile, Kenneth came down to the lobby. We didn't have anything planned for the day, so we decided to walk to Ipanema Beach, and then go to the parade. We both had tickets to the Samba Parade, and this parade would last throughout the night. Different Samba schools practice all year long in order to march in competition wearing lavish costumes.

We left the hotel and began to walk down Copacabana Beach. The day was sunny, and there were a lot of *cariocas* playing soccer in the sand on the beach for recreation. They play hard and they are very good at the game. Also, they play beach volley ball and paddle ball. The women usually sit out and sun-drench until their bodies are hot with heat, then they would get up and take a dip in the South Atlantic Ocean. The beaches were beautiful and clean. It was summer time in Brazil, and with everyone outside, the beaches were crowded with tourists and families. I was never a "beach person" myself, but just walking along the beach front next to the ocean was a great experience. Kenneth brought a little map, and we followed it to Ipanema Beach. We remembered the famous song, *The Girl from Ipanema*, written years ago. Ipanema is more of an upscale place than Copacabana Beach, and the area seemed a lot safer.

We walked around Ipanema, stopped at a restaurant for lunch and stayed around for most of a day. It wasn't as crowded as Copacabana, and that made it more relaxing. There were no kids coming up to us and begging for money, and the beach wasn't as crowded, but there were a few pretty Brazilian women sun-tanning on the beach. It was good to venture out of Copacabana and see another area. I liked Ipanema; there was something about it that seemed comfortable to me.

After the sun began to set, we started back to Copacabana Beach, about a twenty-minute walk. We saw a lot of merchants selling all kinds of items. I wanted to buy my mother a beautiful picture of Rio de Janeiro. I got a good bargain. We went back to the hotel and got ready to go to the parade. It looked like it might rain.

Clouds would form and then disappear. We got something to eat from the hotel then waited for the bus. Eventually the bus came, about 9:00PM. The tour guide said the Samba Parade was going all night, and the bus would make trips back to the hotel if necessary, when enough people wanted to leave. On the way to the Samba Parade there was a lot of traffic. It took about forty-five minutes. When we arrived, there were mobs of people hanging around outside the parade area.

Once inside, the pageant was a sight to see. They marched down the middle of the street. The street path was well lit, and their beautiful costumes shone in different designs and colors. I was amazed at the creativity. Also the Brazilian women in the different Samba schools were very beautiful, even from a distance. It started to rain a little bit, off and on. We stayed until about midnight and then decided to go back to the hotel. We went to the bus and waited for some more people to come. Eventually we left about 12:30PM or so.

Copacabana Beach at night is very beautiful. The Christ statue lights up the sky, and the green street lights below make an amazing, almost magical contrast.

Fat Tuesday had arrived, the last day before Ash Wednesday when fasting for the season of Lent begins. After Lent, it is the Easter holiday. We woke about 9:00AM the next morning and went to the lobby for breakfast. We talked about this day being the last day of Carnival and wanting to have an especially good time.

The Monte Libano Ball was that evening, and we were looking forward to it. After breakfast, Kenneth and I walked around the beach front and then decided to go to Michael's hotel. Michael said he had no plans for the evening. We said that we were going to Monte Libano to a ball. He said he would hang around Copacabana. He brought a video camera with him and wanted to film Brazilian women lying down and walking on the beach. Michael was having a fun time. He asked us if we had any problems with the Brazilians. I told him that we had no problems at all, probably because we were both African Americans. But Michael was an American, and stood out and was a target for burglary. I told him to watch his back, just as if he were in the States.

After talking with Michael, we headed back to the hotel. It was lunch time, so we ate lunch there. While eating, Gus came out and we said we would see him at Monte Libano. He said he would look for us and then he left. I went back inside to take a nap. Before I knew it, it was nightfall. I woke and got ready to go out. My body was tired and had never really gotten used to the time difference. But this was the last night to enjoy myself in Rio de Janeiro, and I was going to do just that.

Kenneth had been napping too; he had gotten up and was getting ready to go. We were both hungry.

We left the hotel together and went to a sidewalk cafe to order some dinner. The place was packed full of people. Brazil has some really good food. Anyway, while waiting for our dinner, Kenneth noticed a girl on the other side of the cafe. A man nearby walked past our table selling flowers, and Kenneth bought her a flower and sent it to her table. Right away she came over, and she could speak English! The girl was from Germany and visiting Rio de Janeiro for the

Carnival. She had a pretty face and a decent body. She and Kenneth began to talk, and when we finished dinner, I was ready to go to Monte Libano for the ball. Kenneth's new friend didn't have a ticket, and Kenneth said he would pay her way in. We stopped a taxi and away we went.

When we got there, Kenneth bought her a ticket, and we went in. It was about 9:30PM. We walked around inside the ballroom. It was a huge building shaped like a square with different levels. It was big, the music was loud and, once again, the Brazilian women were there. It was a little early for the ball to be going full blast. Anyway, about 10:00PM, Kenneth said, "Hey, I'm leaving with her and going back to Copacabana Beach.'

"Okay," I said, "I'll catch you later on tonight."

He was gone. I went outside the building to get some air and orient myself. Cars and taxis arrived at the ball, and beautiful women got out of the vehicles, dressed in incredible costumes and fine dresses. This ball was different from the others I had attended. The women at this ball were more elegant and carried themselves with a kind of reserve or dignity. They had class. After about an hour of just looking at the women going inside the place, I decided to go back in. This time, the main floor was packed and everybody was dancing. There were topless dancers, but not as many as before. Around midnight, I thought about leaving to catch up to Kenneth. I would have to catch a cab back to Copacabana Beach. I decided to wait. I continued to walk around the club. It was now 1:00AM, and I knew that I should go back across town. Then I saw Gus. He was dancing with a very pretty woman, and he seemed to be having a good time. I talked to him for a few minutes.

Before I knew it, it was 2:00AM. For some reason I couldn't leave this place... It was as if a kind of soulful force was keeping me there. I didn't really understand it.

It was now 4:00AM, and I knew that I had to go. It was really late and I had been walking around the ballroom for nearly five hours. As I walked around the corner of the ballroom, I saw her. She was standing in a little corner section of this enormous ballroom, and I stopped and asked her name.

She said, "Therezinha."

And without a thought, I said, "You're beautiful."

Therezinha had a girlfriend with her. Her name was Ana, and Ana could speak English. Therezinha could not. She had big, round brown eyes that a man could disappear into, and pretty coffee mocha-colored skin and long black silky hair. She was stunning. Her friend Ana asked where I was staying and I told her Copacabana Beach. And she said, "We are getting ready to go too. We can get a taxi together and drop you off." That was great, because I was a little concerned about getting out of there anyhow and trying to talk to taxi drivers in order to get back to my hotel.

We left the ball and got in the cab and went to the Hotel California. The three of us went into the lobby. I left them to go to my room to get a camera. We took pictures in the lobby and exchanged telephone numbers and addresses. Therezinha told Ana to tell me that she would call the hotel the next day and we could go to the beach.

By now it was around 5:00AM. The sun was beginning to rise above Copacabana Beach. It was also Ash Wednesday and Carnival was over. I looked outside and saw the beginning of light in the sky. The day was going to be beautiful, I could tell—the sky was orange and reflected off the water in wonderful pastel colors.

We went out front to get a taxi. The doorman got us one and as they loaded into the cab, I gave Therezinha a kiss on each cheek. At that moment, she actually reminded me of a princess. The taxi began to pull away, and Therezinha turned to wave back at me through the rear window. From that moment on, I knew that something about Therezinha was special. I wanted to see her again.

Chapter
Three

I went back to the room. I wasn't even tired. Kenneth had still not made it back. I was sure that he was doing just fine wherever he was. I decided to go to the hotel lobby for breakfast. They were setting up for the morning breakfast when Kenneth walked in.

"Hey, where have you been, buddy?"

Kenneth told me that he was at a club with his German friend, and they had been dancing all night long. He also said that he had seen my friend Michael, and Michael took some pictures of them.

"Let's sit down for breakfast." We sat down and began to talk about the night before.

"I met a beautiful Brazilian woman last night at Monte Libano," I said. "Her name is Therezinha and we took pictures here in the hotel. She and her girlfriend just left about a half an hour ago."

Kenneth was surprised. He asked, "Did more women come to the ball?"

I told Kenneth that it was packed. "You can't imagine how fine the women were!"

After breakfast we went to the room.

"I'm going to see Therezinha later today. She said she would call the hotel about 1:00PM."

Kenneth nodded, "She did?"

I was getting tired after eating breakfast and decided to lie down for awhile. I figured that by the time I woke up, Therezinha would call and we could go to the beach. The thought of her call excited me. Not only did she have a beautiful face, but also her body was just as beautiful. She was a full-figured woman, and I wanted to see her in one of those Brazilian bikinis. Just the thought of seeing her in one of those bikinis turned me on.

About 2:00PM, I woke. Kenneth was still asleep. The phone in our room hadn't rung. About a half hour later, Kenneth woke and said, "I'm hungry, let's go and have lunch." So we got up and left the hotel. I told the clerk in the lobby to take a message if anyone called for me.

We left and started walking down Copacabana Beach. We stopped at a sidewalk cafe to order lunch. We sat at an outside table, and Sage and Johnny noticed us. They came over.

We said, "Join us for lunch."

As we ate, all four of us talked about our experiences in Rio. We all agreed that Rio had provided us a great vacation. We were all leaving the next day, Thursday, and none of us wanted to leave. Especially me. Since I had met Therezinha, I wanted the opportunity to spend some time with her and get to know her.

After lunch, the four of us walked around Copacabana Beach, just enjoying the air off the ocean. Copacabana was really quiet. It was Ash Wednesday, and everybody was either at Mass or some other church service. I could recognize that the city of Rio de Janeiro was beginning to return to normal. Many of the tourists were gone already. The outdoor cafes were bare. The feeling of excitement of Carnival had left the air. It was over until next year, when it would start all over again. It's part of their custom as a third-world country, and with the international debt and their own economic problems, the people need something to make them forget about their problems, at least for a few days.

It was about 5:00PM and the sun was setting. I wondered if Therezinha had called our room. Sage and Johnny had left, and Kenneth and I returned to the hotel. I checked at the desk, and there were no messages. I went to our room very disappointed. After all, she said she would call…

Anyway, I started packing my suitcase. There was nothing planned for the evening, and tomorrow we had a long flight ahead of us. Kenneth decided to pack also. When we were finished, we left for the same restaurant where we had eaten steak and lobster on our first night and to celebrate the end of a wonderful vacation. Moreover, Kenneth and I had gotten along very well, and we enjoyed each other's company and came to know that we could trust one another. After dinner, we returned directly to our hotel.

The next thing I remember, it was morning. We woke about 9:00AM, went to the lobby and had a big breakfast. We returned to the room and I called the tour company to tell them to pick us up and take us to the airport. We were already packed and ready to go. Then we went out to the front of the hotel and sat down. Neither of us wanted to talk; we just sat quietly and thought about things. I began to think about going back to work. There were so many things for me to do once I got back... Gus passed by, and we told him that we were leaving. He said that he enjoyed meeting us. I asked him if he had had a good time the other night at Monte Libano. He said he did.

"Me too," I replied, "I met a beautiful woman there that night."

Gus smiled and said, "Lucky you!"

Gus left and then Angela came by. She sat down and she and Kenneth started talking. I didn't join the conversation; I just looked across the way at the beach and the water and thought, 'What an incredible and beautiful country I'm leaving.'

We had lunch at the hotel, and shortly after, we checked out of the hotel and waited for the bus. When Toni, our tour guide, finally arrived, we headed for the airport. Sage and Johnny also were on the bus. The four of us talked for awhile, and then checked in. We boarded the plane for Miami International. It was a good flight back to Miami, and from there we flew back to San Francisco.

It was good to be back home. Everything was okay with my business—no buses had broken down and the drivers kept their schedules. That was good news. Later that night, I went to my mother's house and gave her the picture I bought for her.

She thanked me and hung it on the wall right away. She liked the picture. It was a grand souvenir: a large, brightly-colored Brazilian bird, which looked like a parrot, sitting in a tree. In the background was Sugarloaf Mountain and Corcovado, Christ the Redeemer, and between the two mountains, there was blue-green water. In the distance was the cityscape of Rio de Janeiro. My mother smiled as she looked at the picture. And now that she knew I was back home safe, she was happy that I had traveled abroad.

Over the next week, I had a chance to show my friends some pictures of the women in Brazil. They went crazy over the pictures. Every time I showed the Carnival photos, I repeated, "You would have to be there to really enjoy Rio."

I kept the pictures of Therezinha and her friend Ana to myself. I thought about Therezinha all the time.

*****

It was a Saturday morning. By then I had been home for about a month. It was early and the phone rang loudly. I woke up thinking, 'Who's calling me this early on a Saturday morning?' I answered the phone. It was a long-distance overseas operator, who said, "Collect call from Therezinha?"

I said, "Yes, I will accept it!"

Therezinha's cousin Marcia was on the other end; she said that she would translate for us. Marcia was a school teacher and spoke English well. She was also very nice. Marcia said that Therezinha was calling to say hello to me. I told her that I missed her. Marcia said that Therezinha apologized for not having called the hotel the next day as she said she would. She had misplaced the phone number, and by the time she had found it, I had already left Brazil. The explanation made me feel good. Therezinha looked so honest and sweet to me, and I felt that something must have happened that day in Rio de Janeiro for her not to have called. I asked Therezinha to write me a letter and I would write back to her. She said she would write to me. After that, Marcia said goodbye, and I hung up the phone. I was wide awake now, sitting up in bed, thinking.

'Wow! Therezinha called me all the way from Brazil!'

In about a week I expected to get my first letter from her. Three weeks later, it finally came. It was now April. Therezinha wrote that she had to get help in order to write the letter. It must have been difficult for her. She said that she was very happy with our phone conversation, with her cousin Marcia's help, and that she was happy that she met me that night at Monte Libano. She said that she wished we had spent more time together to get to know one another better. I thought the same. She said that she was looking for a job, but she hadn't found one at that time, and she would keep looking until she had found one. She then asked if I would send her copies of the pictures we had taken at the Hotel California. She closed the letter by saying that she's waiting for my answer.

"Kisses, Therezinha."

The very next day I had negatives made of the hotel pictures. There was one picture of her sitting down in a chair in the lobby. I bought a card with a picture slot in it and sent it to her. I also sent pictures of my car and house. This was exciting to me, sending a letter to someone in another country, and especially exciting was the fact that

I was writing to Therezinha. Of all the women that I had seen in Brazil, none of them had mesmerized me as much as she did.

Therezinha

I was very happy when I received Kevin's first letter and the pictures. I felt that it could be the beginning of a great friendship. My cousin Marcia translated the letter for me. It was too early to think of a relationship. I wasn't sure whether I was going to get a letter back. I thought Kevin was just a tourist who wanted to take a picture to remember the country where he had vacationed.

It was July before I received the next letter from Therezinha. She had found a job! I was very happy for her. She told me about her family. She had four sisters and two brothers—a big family. Her dad was a lawyer. Therezinha was twenty-seven years old, and she had no children. Now I knew that I was one year older than she. She asked me to tell her more about my family, and she wanted to know more about me. She finally closed her letter to me with the word "Kisses." I wished that I could fly back to Rio and receive a kiss from her. She seemed to be honest and sincere with me in her letters. This was important to me. If our friendship was going to last, both of us had to be open and honest with one another. I wrote her back and told her about my family, also a big family like hers, and more about myself.

I was certain that I wanted to see Therezinha again. Since I could not go back to Rio de Janeiro, the next best thing was for her to come visit me. I offered to buy her ticket, because I knew that she had just started working and didn't have much money. I wasn't sure how she would react to this invitation, but I invited her anyway. The invitation suggested the month of December.

About a month later, I received a response from Therezinha. As I opened the envelope, I wondered what her answer would be to my invitation. She said that she was glad to have received the invitation, but she couldn't tell me whether or not she would be able to come at the time of the letter. She acknowledged that I would buy her ticket for her, but she was shy about that fact. Further, she would also have to convince her parents about my sincerity. Otherwise, they would be worried about their daughter, who couldn't speak English and would be totally lost in terms of communicating in a foreign country. And I couldn't speak Portuguese, which didn't help the situation.

But Therezinha did write that one of her dreams was to see the United States and perhaps even be able to live there some day. When I read that comment, I thought that maybe I could be the "one" for her and make her dreams come true. She asked if there were many Brazilians in California and if the people of California treated them in a civilized way. She mentioned that she knew some friends in the United States, and some day she would like to visit them.

Well, she closed the letter with the possibility of her coming to visit in December. I thought to myself that a December visit would be good for me. School would be out for Christmas vacation, and I would have time to show her around the state. Two weeks later, another letter came from Therezinha. It was a birthday card, since it was my birthday. The card read, "I hope that next year we can celebrate your birthday together." As usual now, she closed the letter "Kisses, Therezinha."

I knew that the friendship we had started was getting stronger with every letter. At the time, I didn't have anyone special in my life. I just worked long hours and went home. When one is self-employed, work takes up all of one's time. There's no time to go out in the evenings to look for girlfriends, not that I wanted to. I had always wanted to find that special "someone," and I was a lonely man. My business kept my time filled, and I was always on the run. But it was still obvious to me that I wasn't really happy with my situation, in terms of romance.

I started to think that the pen-pal friendship with Therezinha was a positive thing for me—and for her. But why did she have to be so far away? It bothered me. Therezinha was unreachable; thousands of miles separated us. A little time passed, and again the phone rang early one Saturday morning. I woke thinking it could be Therezinha.

"Hello!"

It was the overseas operator again, with a collect call from Therezinha.

"Yes," I said, half asleep. Her cousin Marcia was on the phone, ready to translate again. She told me that Therezinha would not be able to come to California in December. There were problems with the visa, and her new position didn't allow vacation time until next year in May.

I was very disappointed with the news. I understood the situation, but at the same time I wanted her to come visit me; we could enjoy Christmas and New Year's together. I also knew that Immigration posed a big problem with our relationship, because she had to get a visa and that was very difficult for her. After Marcia translated the bad news, I told her to tell Therezinha to take care and that I would talk to her later. Marcia said okay and hung up. Well, another lonely Christmas and New Year's, with nobody to hold on to. I was angry for awhile, but there was nothing I could do to change the situation. I had to accept the fact that Therezinha wasn't coming for Christmas.

Now more than ever, I wanted to get Therezinha something special for Christmas. I went to the bank and got an international money order for $100 to send. She had never asked me for money or anything else. I mailed my gift to Therezinha.

The holiday season moved ahead. A few days before Christmas, I bumped into an old high school friend of mine, Trudy. Trudy had been staying up north, about an eight-hour drive from San Francisco. She asked me what my plans were for Christmas.

I replied, "Nothing. I was expecting a friend of mine to visit from Brazil, but she is not coming."

Trudy asked if I would like to ride up north and spend Christmas with her and her children. She had been divorced for a few years by now. Trudy had a big place, school would be out, and her children would be home. Well, Therezinha wasn't coming, and I thought the change would be good for me. I decided to drive up north and have a white Christmas, with the heavy snows of the Pacific Northwest falling across the hillsides and clinging to the trees.

As I had hoped, snow was everywhere. I really enjoyed myself. Trudy's three children, Caroline, Bobby and Carmen, were great, very nice kids. I had plenty of great company. Still, I thought of Therezinha and how she might be spending the holidays.

New Year's day, 1989 arrived.

"Wow, a new year is upon us already."

A few weeks later, I received a letter from Therezinha. She thanked me for the money. She said that she bought a beautiful dress for a

New Year's Eve party. Her letter suggested that she was a lot happier than she had been in the last few months. She invited me to return to Brazil next month for Carnival so that we might get to know one another better. She had also sent me some pictures of her sisters and her friend Ana.

Well, Carnival in Rio was about a month away, and there was no way that I could go. Not at that time. My business had acquired more contracts, and I hadn't enough drivers to cover their schedules as well as mine, if I were to leave. I would have made arrangements if Therezinha had invited me earlier. Too late to make arrangements.

By now, it had been almost a year since we had met that night at Monte Libano. I wanted Therezinha with me, but I was beginning to think that it would never happen. There were just too many obstacles, and I was afraid we wouldn't be able to overcome them. I couldn't go to Rio de Janeiro when she wanted me to visit, and she couldn't come to see me when I wanted her to visit. The situation was depressing because we couldn't be together when we desired each other. I didn't know how to handle the situation—if she wasn't 6,500 miles away, Therezinha and I would be together. I came to think that the whole idea was just a fantasy; in reality, we would never ever see each other again.

Chapter
Four

In the next two months, my whole life changed. Trudy and I had gotten closer during this period, and she even asked me to marry her. Trudy was a good-looking woman with a good business mind. As a businessman, I began to think how important it was to have a wife who understands what it takes to build a company, where you have the final responsibility for everything that happens. Perhaps we could even build something up together, if we did get married. And I loved her kids. They were always great to be around. Trudy's children were well-behaved and respectful. To be honest, I had feelings for Trudy, but those feelings did not compare to the feelings I had for Therezinha.

During those months I hadn't written to Therezinha, and I felt out of touch with her. I was very confused during this time. Financially, I was doing well, but I didn't have the one woman who would make my life complete. I wanted to get married, I knew that much. And Trudy was there, right in front of me. She was willing and ready to get married again. I had a decision to make, and it was just a matter of time before I would.

One afternoon, the phone rang.

"Hello?"

The call was from someone named Duane. He was from
Oakland, a city next to San Francisco. He and his wife had just
returned from Carnival in Rio de Janeiro, and he told me that he
had met Therezinha and Ana. Therezinha had told him about me
and asked that he call me for her and say hello. What a small
world! Duane and I talked for a little while. He said that he
enjoyed Carnival and that he wanted to go back next year. I
thanked him for calling me and hung up the phone. Wow, I
wished that I could have been there. Therezinha and I would
have had a good time together.

About a week later, I received a letter and a picture from Therezinha.
She was dressed in costume, and the fantastic colors of the Carnival
parade were in the background. Her picture was one of stunning
beauty. My mind drifted back to Brazil and then back to the present.
She had noticed that I had not written to her lately, and she was
wondering if I was alright and if everything was going okay in my
life. Once again, she closed her letter to me by saying, "Kisses."
This time she added, "Don't forget me."

I knew that I had to tell her I was planning to get married. I cared
too much for her to not tell her. She deserved to know. I decided
that I would buy a house before Trudy and I got married. It was a
twenty-acre ranch. Trudy loved animals and she needed land. She
had goats, dogs, horses, cats, you name it. The property was about
a three-hour drive from my place of business. Trudy had found the
property and set the terms of the sale. She was good at negotiating
deals with people. All I had to do was, simply, put up the money,

and the deal was done. The house was an old, three-bedroom farmhouse that needed work, but it was fixable.

The next three months went by very fast. We set a wedding date of August, and all of a sudden, it was June. School was about to get out, but my summer schedule was going to be just as busy as in the fall or winter. Since the house was so far away, Trudy and I decided to turn my duplex into my office, and I would stay there during the week and go home on the weekends. Trudy wasn't happy about this, but it was too far to commute.

Also in June I received another letter from Therezinha. She wanted to know why I hadn't written to her. Her mother had been sick, and she had been taking care of her. She was still working at her job. She asked me to write back to her and tell her what was going on with me. She was anxious to know about me. She knew something was wrong.

Two days after her letter to me, my brother Alvis and I went to lunch. I told him about the correspondence. I just couldn't put it off any longer. My brother told me to do it right away.

"Do it now. She needs to know, Kevin."

He was right. There was no other way but to tell her myself.

A week later I wrote Therezinha a letter. I knew that she would be hurt by my decision. I wished her the best, because she deserved the best. It was the saddest letter I ever had to write in my life. It felt even worse when I slipped the letter in the mailbox, because then I knew that she would be receiving it.

August had arrived already. There was still so much yet to do, but as planned, it was time for Trudy and me to get married. Planning for the wedding had been very stressful. I had to finance the whole thing, along with my parents, and they weren't too happy about it. Anyway, our wedding day had arrived. Trudy was an hour late getting to the church, which was already full of family and friends. I was in the back of the church with the pastor, thinking that if she didn't show up, I would just sneak out of the church and drive away. I didn't want to stand in front of the congregation, face everybody and say, "I'm sorry, but you will all have to go home now."

Trudy finally showed up. There was tension in the air. Everybody was uptight, even after the marriage ceremony. We went to the reception. People were eating and talking, but they didn't seem happy. Instead of a wedding, it seemed more like a gathering for a funeral. After the reception, we left for our honeymoon. We flew to Hawaii and stayed on the island of Kauai. Kauai offered a more quiet and gentle atmosphere than the main island. Every inch of the island was green; it rains a lot there, as it did when we were honeymooning, and it was very hot. But I enjoyed the time we spent there, walking around the area, taking in the scenic views that were everywhere, and visiting Waiamia Canyon, a canyon similar to the Grand Canyon, but of course, smaller.

Therezinha
I was upset when I heard of Kevin's marriage plans, but I was also happy for him at the same time. I really wanted him to be happy. Somehow I expected it to happen, due to the great distance between us. I new little about Kevin, what I knew of Kevin was only through the cards and letters I got from him. But he seemed to be very sincere. My friend Ana translated our letters.

When I returned home to my office after my honeymoon, there was a letter from Therezinha. I knew by now that she had received my letter. The letter waiting for me was a birthday card. She said that she was sad about the news of my marriage plans, but she wished me well nonetheless. I thought to myself that Therezinha was one-of-a-kind. I could never forget her, not even in a thousand years, not even if I lived to be as old as Methuselah.

The next four months were busy. Trudy wanted to board horses as a business. Race horses run for six months on the track, and then they rest for six months. She wanted to build a horse-boarding business for racetrack horses. She knew a little about the game of horse-racing and wanted to make a business from that base of knowledge. We had twenty acres to make use of, so I borrowed money from my family and friends and hired a contractor to build a barn. My dad designed a twenty-stall barn, with automatic waters in each stall, and a hay loft atop the barn. The total size was about 4,000 square feet. It was 22 feet high and 120 feet in length. We painted it red with white trim, and it looked great. Compared to the other farms around the area, the barn was huge and soon became the talk of the little town nearby.

My business was going well. I now had ten buses and ten drivers. My expenditures were up dramatically because I was funding projects at both ends. When the barn was complete and she got her business going, Trudy would subsidize what I was already doing. That would take some of the financial pressure from me. There were other things that needed to be done around the ranch in order to get the business ready for horse-boarding. There had to be a boarded fence on the front side of the property, and I boarded ten acres of fence. This would protect the horses from running into the wire that was now surrounding it. Also, a quarter-mile track had to be installed so that the horses could be exercised, and an exercise arena needed to be built too. I then decided to fix up the old, three-bedroom farmhouse and paint it red with white trim, as I did with the barn. "Trudy's Horse Paradise" was the name. Boarding horses was the game. All of this was done on ten of the twenty acres. The ten adjacent acres had a creek flowing through it. It was our plan to build a house on that acreage once the horse-boarding business was established.

October of that year, 1989, was the year San Francisco experienced a major earthquake. The earthquake didn't affect the area where I lived or where my buses were located, but it did cause "down" time for my business. The schools weren't taking many field trips, and many of the freeways and secondary roads were either damaged or were unable to be reached by way of major freeways.

At the beginning of December, I sent off an early Christmas card to Therezinha. I had thought of her often during the past four months of my marriage. I had flashbacks of the past. She sent me back a Christmas card. She had heard of the earthquake in San Francisco and had tried to call me but couldn't reach me. She was very happy now that she had received my letter and knew that I was okay. Therezinha wrote that she wanted to make a change, in terms of bettering her life, but was not quite sure of how to go about doing it. I thought to myself that it wouldn't be long before she would get married. I had written to her in past letters that she was a special person in my life. In December's letter, she again said that she was proud to be special. She wished that we could continue that other part of our relationship, the romantic part, but realized that it was too late for us.

It was 1990 already. It had been a rough ending to the previous year. The barn was almost complete. I was anticipating that the ranch would be making some money by now. In San Francisco, I had to train new drivers because some were leaving. Once the barn was complete, hopefully in June, boarder clients would come. During this time, I was supporting the whole family and both residences. And we had a zoo of animals. Hay was costing me $125.00 a ton for alfalfa, the best. It was no easy job.

June arrived and the barn was completely built, but it was empty still.

My frustration with the pressures of financing everything, with no end in sight that things might change built. One night I told Trudy my feelings.

"We've got to get something going with this barn. I can't afford to have this barn empty. It's costing too much on both ends. This is the dream you said you wanted. Now do something with it!"

In August, I received a birthday card from Therezinha. She always remembered my birthday, and I looked forward to her card. The pleasure I felt when I heard from her never lessened.

The summer months were very busy for my business, thank God, because my bills were stacking up. All of my money was going one way with no return. The business at the ranch was not going to happen. I had to admit that to myself. Trudy couldn't get it started, and it was useless to stay there any longer. My bills had skyrocketed as a result of the property, and Trudy didn't want to stay there any longer either. She wanted to move to the Southwest where it was cheaper to live, she claimed. I knew that I had to do something. So, we packed up at the end of August and I put the house up for sale. I had no choice. About that same time, the bottom had fallen out of the real estate market. For several years the market had been over-priced, and now it was catching up with itself. This was bad news for me, because I was in a great deal of trouble financially. I simply had to cut my overhead and fast! Why me, why me?

We boarded all of the animals, and Trudy and the children moved closer to my business in San Francisco.

Summer was over, and by the time November arrived, Trudy had finally convinced me to move her to the desert. She was unhappy and she would continue to be unhappy until she moved. We loaded up the animals and I rented a U-Haul truck and had a friend of mine, Richard, drive it to the Southwest—that's where she wanted to go. I drove our truck, and the three dogs we had were with us in the truck. We took our time driving because of the dogs. Finally, we got to our destination, and soon the U-Haul truck also arrived. But there was a problem once we arrived. The people to whom we had sent a down-payment to secure the house told us that they wouldn't rent it to us because of the animals. But we knew better—it was because of our color. Eventually, we found a nice place, but it was more expensive than I anticipated. Now, more than ever, I was hoping that the house in California would sell.

After Trudy and the children settled in, I left for California. I was very unhappy with the whole situation. Life had become a nightmare in the daytime. I was trying to juggle my business and my family, and both were in trouble. I was stressed out to the max. It was terrible. Then, one month later, a disaster happened. In December of 1990, a driver of mine caused me to lose a $50,000 contract because he was having personal problems and did not show up at work on time. Now I was really in trouble with my finances!

Christmastime approached. Everything continued to go wrong, and the holidays were miserable. I was very unhappy and upset about everything. During those times, I would think about Therezinha and would smile at the very thought of her. I hoped that she was alright and that she was happy. That was the main thing, wishing that she was happy, even though I was sad.

After Christmas, I returned to California. The house still hadn't been sold. We had offers, but nothing solid. The business was just rolling along, and I was barely able to pay bills. It was now 1991 and I was hoping and praying for a better year. I was starting off the year $50,000 in the hole and my morale was really down.

I couldn't get over the fact that I had lost one of the biggest and best contracts of my business. The contract had been with the school where everything had started for me. And now I didn't want the rest of my business and my married life to fall down around me. I prepared myself for the fact that it was going to be really hard to run my business with my family in the Southwest. I would have to fly down there on the weekends. That kind of running around and flying back and forth was sure to take a toll on my mind and body. I had hoped that things would get better in 1991, and my life would get straightened out.

Chapter
Five

The weeks went by quickly. February came, and the house was still sitting on the market. No buyers at all. It was wintertime and the slow economy didn't help the matter. It was bad. No one was spending any money. The monthly payments on the house in the desert where we were living were astronomically high, considering we were only renting. I must admit, however, that the house did have everything. It sat on five acres and fruit trees surrounded the property. The house had a two-car garage, security gates, a circular driveway, a huge fireplace, a breakfast room and a swimming pool with a waterfall. It even had dog kennels. It was a very nice property indeed. I had thought someday I would like to build a house similar to that one.

But Trudy still wasn't working. I couldn't afford the place; we had to move. She understood.

The next weekend was a holiday weekend, and Trudy had found another place for us to move. Although it was a small house, there was room for the animals and we had no choice—we took it. We had a lot of packing to do. The kids all helped and we began to move to the new place. It was about thirty minutes away from where we were living. Back and forth we went that whole weekend until we were done. Monday had arrived, and I flew back to California. At least we were completely moved, and I could now cut my rent expenses a little. I still hadn't made up the deficit from the lost contract, but I was doing my best to keep everything and everybody happy as much as I could, considering I was on the verge of bankruptcy.

April came, and I spent the Easter weekend with the family. Money problems continued. There was always food in the house—that was not a problem—but I couldn't take care of my other obligations until the house was sold. Since it was springtime, I had hoped that the market would pick up and I would get some legitimate offers on the ranch. Around this time Trudy told me that she wanted to move farther down south. She didn't want to stay in the desert anymore, and she wanted to leave right away.

"You have to let the kids finish the school year first," I said. I thought to myself, 'Here we go again.'

I did have a chance to relax a little bit, even though my mind was busy with the business and the family problems. The next two months went by fairly quickly, and it was now June. Trudy was ready to go down south.

She said, "It's cheaper to live down there and I could find work more easily."

After much prodding, she convinced me.

We loaded up the car, the truck, and rented a second truck. I hired a driver to help drive them down south. Since it was summer, I was very busy with field trips and had to stay in San Francisco. I wasn't sure when I was going to be able to see Trudy and the children again that summer. I wasn't happy with the fact that she was leaving the desert, but she wouldn't stay. Her mind was made up. I was very worried about them, especially as they drove down, but there were no problems.

Trudy found a place, and she and the children moved in. I planned to go down and visit in July. I flew down that month. When I got to the airport, Trudy picked me up and we went to the house. It was an old Confederate Wartime house. It was big, and it had a lot of land around it. The house was quite a ways out in the country. At night, it was black dark at the house. There were railroad tracks in front of the house, and a train would come by in the middle of the night making a lot of noise. It was summer and very humid. The kids didn't seem to mind. Kids are like that—they adjust to all kinds of situations that are presented to them, as long as they can have fun. Personally, I thought the rent was too high, especially since the house looked as if it had been around since the 1800s.

By coincidence, my sister's home was not far from the property. That same weekend Trudy and I drove to my sister Linda's house, which was about an hour away. Her home was in a lovely, well-kept suburb filled with big homes. Linda is very smart. She is an electrical engineer, and I respect her very much.

We arrived in the early evening. We walked in through the garage. It was open and a car was parked there, next to the house. I thought that it must be Willy's, Linda's husband. He is a car salesmen, one of the best in their region of the state and a really nice guy. Their home is a tri-level, handsomely constructed, and the rooms are beautifully furnished. Linda was so surprised I had come to visit. They had company at the time, and we joined the group, talking and eating and really enjoyed each other all night long. We finally had to leave and head back to the house. We thanked them for everything and left. I hadn't seen Linda for a long time and it brought back good memories. Trudy and I made it back home. It had been a long but enjoyable day.

The next day, Trudy said that she would bake a blueberry pie and a blackberry pie. The kids were already outside, picking the berries for the pies. Trudy was an excellent cook; she could cook practically anything from scratch. The kitchen was "hers," and she knew what to do in the kitchen. Unfortunately for me, I never got much of a chance to eat her cooking. I was always at work, trying to support her and the family. The animals ate better than I did. I didn't like that fact, but it was true.

After dinner, we ate our slices of pie and they were good…I was stuffed! Everybody liked Trudy's pies, they were fabulous! Then the kids and I watched TV for the rest of the night. The next day, I had a talk with Trudy about the house. I told her that I didn't like the house and that she could have found something closer and cheaper. She said she would look and find something better.

I said, "Look right away."

I planned to leave the next day for California. There was a lot of work waiting for me back in San Francisco, and a summer schedule to fulfill. On my last day, I stayed around the house and spent time with the children. Even though I wasn't around that much, we would always have dinner together like a regular family. I taught the kids to say their blessing before eating, and they started taking turns saying the dinner blessing. I also took them to church when I could. Just being around them was good for me—they were fun to be with and I cared very much for them.

When a man marries into a ready-made family, often the kids don't like the man, and they cause trouble for him. This leads to trouble in the relationship with the mother. I didn't have that trouble at all, and I never caused any hurtful feelings, and the children knew it.

I started getting my things together that night. I didn't know when I would return. I wanted Trudy to come back to California, but I couldn't convince her. So, I could only hope that she would find a better place to live than that old Confederate house. It had been a hot and enjoyable day, and I especially enjoyed being with the kids. In fact, being with the kids was the best part of it.

When the morning came, I was ready to leave. After breakfast, we left for the airport. Trudy dropped me off. It was hard leaving my family down there, but that was the way Trudy wanted things. To tell the truth, I had so many other issues to deal with back in California that I was happy for the little mini-vacations. Getting away helped me to get a little rest. Things at the business for the most part had gone okay during these weekend trips. But you never know what to expect when you come back. All you can do is hope and pray that everything that was supposed to be done, got done.

About a week later, Trudy called and said that the neighbors had called the Humane Society, and they came and took the animals. They accused Trudy of not feeding them, which was untrue.

She said that she was moving back to the desert and she needed some money to get back there. Once back, she would find an apartment. The house in California still had not sold, and I was beginning to think that it was never going to sell. I was trying to juggle one situation and then another and still keep things going. I was very tired of it all.

About a week before my birthday, I received a birthday card at my office from Therezinha. She wished me a happy birthday and hoped that I and my family were alright. Just the thought of her gave me a really good feeling inside. After all, we hadn't seen each other since that night we first met. Nonetheless, she was stuck in my mind and in my heart. When I thought of Therezinha, it was as if I took a breath of fresh, sweet air after having been in a stuffy chamber. I had to deal with my family situation and try to make it work, but it was not going well between Trudy and me at this time.

I was just tired of everything. It was time for school to start in the desert. She had to register the kids for school, and they needed school clothes. It seemed like there was always something to deal with on both ends, business and family. I began to realize that I had taken on too much at one time.

Unfortunately, the business was still down. I was just hanging on financially, but trying to be positive about the approaching school year and hopeful that the ranch would sell soon. Either that or I would be bankrupt for sure. The house had been on the market for over a year and the economy was still slow. The kids seemed okay; they didn't seem to mind being back in the desert. I was concerned about them, being moved around like baggage. I was driving a lot myself, since I was short on drivers and trying to stay on top of the business. I was running around everywhere, handling everything myself, and it was starting to take its toll on me mentally and physically. It never seemed as if I had any time to relax, I was so busy.

September went by, and October came. We finally received a serious offer on the ranch. The price that was offered would be a "break-even" price. It was the barn, I am sure, that really sold the house. The barn was the best thing about the property. I decided to accept the offer, cut my losses and get out of the mortgage. If my financial situation had been better, I would have held out for a better offer, but I was in no position to do that. By the end of October, the house had finally sold. I managed to pay off some bills, which was very important for me to do, considering how long I had owed some people.

Trudy found yet another house that she wanted to move into. It was a nice house with a swimming pool, backyard, and the house was in a fairly good neighborhood. The kids were happy, since they had much more room. The house was nice and the rent was reasonable.

It was now November, and school was out for Thanksgiving. Thanksgiving dinner was excellent, and I really enjoyed the home-cooked food. Trudy still wasn't working, and I was still under pressure, unhappy and tired of barely making ends meet.

After Thanksgiving, there was more bad news waiting for me. Another contract would be lost in three weeks, right before Christmas. Again my drivers weren't showing up at work on time! I felt that I was losing control of the business. Oh boy! What now?! I knew that it was now going to be difficult to start off the new year.

I told Trudy what had happened and that Christmas this year would again be sad. It was a tough time for me. I flew down for Christmas when school was out. There was tension around the house, and our financial condition was tighter than it had ever been before. I could see Trudy's frustration. The kids were okay. I just wished that I had had more money to spend on them for Christmas. When you see things disintegrating around you, it is not a very good feeling. Our relationship was slowly deteriorating.

Christmas Day came. We opened up a few presents and had a ham for Christmas breakfast. I knew that no matter how hard I tried, nothing seemed to be enough or come out right. It was time for me to face the truth, namely, the marriage was not working. And if I didn't make positive changes right away, I would have nothing left. Trudy and I didn't spend that much time together. We were there, but it seemed that we kept to our own space in the house.

January 1992 had already arrived. It was time for me to leave. I had to try to make something happen. I was no quitter. I would do what I had to do to make it.

Chapter
Six

When I returned to my office at the first of the year, a Christmas card from Therezinha was in my mail. She also had sent a picture. She had cut her hair, and she was a lot thinner. She looked extraordinary—really sexy. She wanted my opinion on her new hair style and look. Her birthday was coming up in a few weeks; so I went to the store, bought a card and wrote to her. I told her that I liked her new look and wished her a happy birthday. I also sent her a picture of me, since she had asked for one.

Things were tough when the school year started up again. I had to rearrange drivers and try to stabilize things, which was no easy task. Money was tight, and I didn't know how I was going to overcome the situation. We had a three-day weekend in January. I flew back down to see Trudy and the kids. Things were the same. Trudy and I were definitely not okay. I didn't like what was happening to us. I guess there are two sides to every story, but, oh well… Our relationship had progressively gotten worse.

The next month I had a week off from work. I flew down again, but it was evident that it was over between Trudy and me. I arrived on Sunday evening.

In the morning, the kids asked me if I would take them to church the following Sunday. There was a church about two blocks away. I grew up in a Presbyterian church, and I know that I have been blessed throughout my life. I wanted to expose the kids to that same possibility in their lives, and for me, my church played a big role.

By that Tuesday, I was pissed off at Trudy and wanted out of there. That was it. But I had made a promise to the kids to take them to church on Sunday. They had nothing to do with the failing relationship, but they could feel the tension and they knew that I would be leaving soon. I stayed there that week in my own space. If Trudy slept in the bedroom, I would sleep in the den and vice versa, but not together, by no means together! The week seemed like a month. I was sad and mad about the whole situation. Three years and nothing to show for it. It was one of the worst feelings I had ever experienced. I felt like a stranger in my own house. I tried to remain calm, but inside I was about to explode with anger. I wanted to explode but couldn't. I didn't want to cause a scene in front of the children. They had experienced enough of that in their lives before me, and I'm a non-violent person. There was nothing I could say or do but just wait.

The children were looking forward to going to church with me on Sunday, and that was the only thing that was keeping me there.

Sunday morning finally came. I woke up the kids and told them to go have breakfast and get ready for church. They did. I put on my suit and we left for church. It was a nice Sunday and a very good church service. We enjoyed it. They knew that after church I'd be leaving; I'd be going back to California and wouldn't be back to see them again. That hurt me inside, because I loved them. There was no use trying to stay with Trudy. It was over for sure. I remember talking to them on the way back home.

"Keep taking turns saying your blessings before you eat," I told them.

"Say your prayers every night before you go to bed and be good to your mother."

We talked about some good times we shared and laughed as we were walking back to the house. They were confused, but they understood. They were strong kids, all three of them. Once we got back to the house, Trudy was mad at me, because I hadn't told her that we were leaving for church. I thought to myself, 'Big deal, who are you?' She was boiling mad. The week had come to an end. She then told the children to stay away from me. What could I say or do? They were her children. I was just happy for our time together that morning. I will always remember that. I started packing.

It was time to go. My flight was in the evening. She wanted me out of the house immediately. She took me to the airport. We didn't talk or look at each other on the way. It took about forty-five minutes. Once there, I got out of the truck, grabbed my luggage out of the back, closed the door and walked toward the terminal…I never looked back. Inside the airport, I asked if I could get an earlier flight out of town. They said they would try to help me. Otherwise, I had to wait about five hours, if they couldn't.

"…all that time, money and effort…"

I was told that I could get a flight in about two hours. Once on the plane, I could feel the heat outside coming through the plane window. I looked out of the window and thought about how I could save my business…some way, somehow.

I caught an "Airporter" from the airport, and after I had paid the fair, I only had five dollars left in my pocket and that was it. I had left the truck with Trudy, so I had nothing at this time. I had already sold the car last month. Boy, was I in bad shape! I didn't even know if the business would make it through the month of June. It was just February. My family life was over. I had to find a way to make it through the month of June.

I started to get back in touch with myself by going back to the Presbyterian Church. The Presbyterian Church was the church of my childhood. I felt that my life was off track and I was derailed. Everything was upside down to me. I had no direction. It felt good to get back to church. They were my family. I told them that my marriage was over, and some people in the church seemed to be happy that the marriage was over. I needed the comfort of the church, it gave me strength to keep fighting straight ahead. It helped me through the worst time of my life. Being raised in the church, I could fall back into it and feel okay. If it wasn't for the grace of God, there was no telling what could have happened to me at that time.

I wrote to Therezinha and told her about my situation. She wrote back. It was Carnival time and I desperately wanted to go there and be with her. But I was broke and couldn't go at that time.

Over the next couple of months, Therezinha and I corresponded frequently. It felt good. We hadn't talked this much in a long time. I told her that I would go to Rio that summer, in early August.

She said, "Okay." I was working real hard to keep the business going. Life had dealt us both challenges and adjustments, but we were still going strong.

Rio in August was an inspiration for me, and the very thought of seeing her again gave me momentum. My summer schedule had lined up and it looked very busy. I was still in trouble financially, but I knew that I could make some money during the summer and could get a little caught up on some bills. I still hurt over my break-up with Trudy and the children. I had tried to do my best for them. There was no way for me to contact them or to see them. She had moved again.

Therezinha

I was very happy and very agitated at the same time. I was going to meet Kevin again after four and a half years. I was very confused at the time and didn't really know what I wanted. There were so many factors involved. I wasn't doing very well emotionally, but I had a good chance of improvement at work. I was very happy to get the letters and beautiful cards Kevin had sent me. Some days I was really down and would feel better after receiving his card. I wondered how a person who knew so little of me could like me so much. I was confused. I wanted to be sure of my feelings toward him.

The weeks passed, and I tried to tie up loose ends. By the second week in August, everything was in place. I was ready to go back to Brazil. After all, it had been four and a half years! As soon as the plane took off from Miami International, my heart started to pound in my chest. I remembered thinking to myself that my fantasy was about to turn into a reality because in eight hours Therezinha and I would see each other again.

Chapter
Seven

"How would she look?"

"How would she think I looked?"

Over and over, my mind wondered about these two questions. It was an exciting feeling to anticipate being together again with Therezinha. Even though we corresponded for years, we knew each other only through our letters, and we had only met once, and had spent only an hour or so together. It was so unusual that I was so attracted to this woman, after having spent such a brief time with her. And now I'm on a plane to Rio de Janeiro to see her—an overwhelming feeling took hold of me. Regardless of what would happen once we met again, I was certain that I had to see her. I thought about our relationship up to that point. We had shared a lot of things with each other over the years.

I finally fell asleep, and the next thing I knew, it was morning. The attendants were about to serve breakfast. After breakfast, I washed up in the plane's lavatory as best I could, considering that a person can hardly move in that tiny compartment. The pilot said we would be landing soon and that we should buckle our seat belts. I knew that Therezinha would be waiting to greet me. The plane landed and I went through Customs, pulled my luggage from the turnstile and walked to the lobby.

Once in the lobby, I saw a huge crowd waiting to greet the passengers of the plane. I looked around for Therezinha. In a few minutes I saw her. We noticed each other immediately. She looked beautiful. I kissed her on each cheek, which is customary when greeting a woman in Brazil. Her friend Ana came to the airport to greet me. Therezinha had brought others: her sister Denise, along with her brother-in-law John. John drove a taxi, and we went out to load ourselves and my luggage into the taxi. Rio de Janeiro was hot, even though it was winter. It felt good to be back. As we drove to the hotel, I looked around at the city and began to remember different places and buildings from my first visit. After about a forty-minute drive, we were at Ipanema Beach. Therezinha had made reservations for me at the Everest Park Hotel. It was a fairly nice hotel situated about a block from the beach.

I hadn't slept very well on the plane, and I felt tired. I'm sure that my strong emotions had also worn me out a little too. Therezinha wanted me to go to her house to meet her family.

I said, "Okay, come back in a couple of hours. I need to take a shower and rest a little."

I thanked her and Ana and Denise for picking me up at the airport.

I went to my room and tossed my suitcase on the bed. The room had a balcony that looked down on Ipanema Beach. I walked out on the balcony and saw that there were a lot of people on the beach. I had only had been to Ipanema Beach once before, and it felt as if I were in totally new surroundings. I thought that it would be fun to find out more about this area.

And Therezinha... Therezinha looked happy to see me, but it had been so long...

Before long, John arrived for me, and we left for Therezinha's house. As John drove us down the streets and onto the highway, I sat in the car and hoped that her family would like me. I was nervous about meeting them. I had heard all about Therezinha's parents from her letters, and I was happy about meeting them. But I was still pretty nervous. We arrived about forty minutes later.

Therezinha lived in the suburbs, not too far from downtown Rio de Janeiro. We went in and I met her father, mother, sisters, brothers— the whole family. It was a very nice house. The colors were warm in the house, and tile floors were especially nice, light and dark colors mixed. It was a very comfortable home. I was happy to have the chance to meet everyone. Therezinha's sisters tried to speak in English as best they could, and I found that I could understand them! It amazed me how well they spoke English. Her sisters made me feel right at home; they were very nice to me. And Ana was there. Whenever I didn't understand something, Ana would translate for me.

Therezinha's mother had made some dinner, so we all sat down at the dinner table. It was exciting to actually have dinner with Therezinha and her family. A Brazilian dinner! In my opinion, Brazilians eat very good food. A lot of the food is prepared with manioc flour, which looks like corn meal. We talked as much as we could throughout dinner, taking turns asking and answering questions. After dinner, we took several pictures. It was fun, and I enjoyed doing it. Then we sat in the living room and listened to some music. Therezinha had brought out some of the letters I had written to her years ago. Wow! She still had everything that I had sent her. I was so happy about that because I also had everything that she had sent to me. It was fun to look at the pictures and read some of those "love letters."

After awhile, it was time to go back to the hotel. Her father and mother were very hospitable to me. I appreciated it very much and thanked her whole family. Therezinha was happy that I enjoyed myself with her family. She said she would call me and we would go out some time this week. She had not made definite plans. She was working and didn't have a lot of time during the week to visit and entertain, and I understood. Anyway, I was back in Brazil and I knew that I certainly would enjoy myself.

John knocked on the door, and we left for the hotel. I felt pretty good about the entire evening, so I went out for a walk before bed. I wanted to get acquainted with the area again.

After breakfast the next day, I walked down to the beach and watched the scenes all around me. The *cariocas* were playing soccer and volleyball. Everything was the same as before. I wanted this time to be somewhat quiet and reflective; I needed to relax and think about how I was going to get Therezinha back again. This was the purpose of the trip—to renew my relationship with her. And after seeing her again, I was still intrigued with her. I knew that I had to go slowly in order to win her heart. I didn't want anyone else. My mind was made up for sure.

I walked around and looked in some shops, then returned to the hotel and rested. I had dinner at a restaurant and listened to the music playing from an old jukebox on the other side of the restaurant. After dinner, I walked down the beach front, and I began to feel comfortable with the area and my surroundings. I had a chance to relax and forget about the business and the problems associated with it. I returned to my room, got ready for bed and fell into a deep, restful sleep.

In the morning, Therezinha called and said hello. She said that she would come to the hotel that evening after work. So, during the day I walked around Ipanema Beach by myself, enjoying the peaceful time alone. Nobody bothered me. Ipanema was a peaceful area, and the crowds were a lot smaller than the crowds I remembered from Carnival. Still, there were a lot of homeless people on the street. I gave money to some of them, and they seemed to appreciate it. Basically, I was just wasting time until the evening.

It got close to the time for Therezinha's visit. I went back to the hotel to shower and get dressed for the evening.

We met in the lobby. It was good to see her. Ana was with her, and John was waiting in the taxi. We left and drove to meet a friend of hers. We drove about thirty minutes to a place called Meier, a busy place that also had a train station in the center of town. We drove through Meier to an elegant apartment building. Therezinha rang the buzzer and we were let in. We walked up three flights of stairs and finally we came to an apartment and went in.

Therezinha introduced me to her friends, Claudio and Selma. Claudio was an engineer for the government of Rio. He spoke perfect English and he had lived in the United States. He had studied in Denver, Colorado. We began to talk. Claudio also played the guitar. He began playing, and we started to sing some American songs. I enjoyed being with Claudio and Selma. Like her husband, Selma was also smart, and she could speak a little English. I was able to talk to her and understand her replies. We continued to talk and sing. The time went by and we had to go. John came to take us home. I said goodbye to Claudio and Selma and we left. John took Ana home and then dropped off Therezinha at her home. I said goodbye to her and she said she would call me on my birthday, which was on Thursday. She had planned to give me a party.

I wanted to show Therezinha how much I cared for her, but I felt somewhat constricted; I could only do so much. We had no privacy because someone was always there for translation.

I didn't do much the next day. I knew my way around the beach front pretty well by now. Time went by slowly. I had dinner at another restaurant I had found that afternoon. The food was good, but I was lonely without Therezinha. I wished that she could have been with me.

The atmosphere is always alive in Rio de Janeiro. Even though it wasn't Carnival time, love was in the air—anyone could feel it.

I watched some TV and finally fell asleep.

When I woke, it was my birthday. I knew that I would spend this day with Therezinha and her family, and I was excited. I hung around the hotel, went for a walk along the beach, looked at all of the beautiful women around me and waited for the evening to come.

Finally the time had arrived. John had come and we left for my birthday party. We arrived at Claudio and Selma's apartment, where the party was going to be held. Therezinha and her family were already there. Ana was there too. Everyone talked and laughed and enjoyed one another. I talked with Claudio while Therezinha was in the kitchen helping Selma with the food for the party. After awhile, we ate from a delicious buffet. Then we took pictures. I was really enjoying myself and happy to be celebrating my birthday in Brazil. Therezinha came out of the kitchen with my birthday cake and placed it on the table. Everyone gathered around and sang "*Happy Birthday*" to me, in English, of course.

I smiled at Therezinha all the while she sang. I made a wish that she and I could be together, and then I blew out the candles. In Brazil, the custom is that the birthday person must eat some cake before anyone else can. So I asked Therezinha to cut me a piece of cake and I ate it. The cake was delicious. Everyone ate slice after slice and talked and laughed. It was only the second time I had been with Therezinha's family. I was so happy that they had come to my party. Therezinha's mother gave me a present and I thanked her. Therezinha had also given me a present, a shirt. I thanked her for the present and the birthday party. She wanted to do that for me, she told Ana. I asked Ana to ask Therezinha if she wanted to go out tomorrow night to dance. Ana asked her.

"Okay, we will go out."

It was now time to go. I thanked everyone for coming and said good night. On the way back to the hotel, I began to think that Therezinha and I needed to begin some personal conversations. We needed to talk about our personal relationship. Up to this time, we really hadn't talked seriously. Oh, well. It had been a long, enjoyable birthday and I was tired.

The next day I decided to walk to Copacabana. Once there, I started to remember Carnival 1988, and the familiarity of the surroundings came back clearly. All of those sidewalk cafes and bars, the beautiful women on the beach and, of course, the string bikinis they wore where you could just about see it all. I walked past the California Hotel and looked inside the lobby. Wow! It seemed like such a long time ago… I decided to stop and have something to drink at one of the sidewalk cafes. Women were looking and smiling at me, but I wasn't interested. I didn't want anyone else, only Therezinha.

I was familiar with Copacabana and enjoyed the nostalgia. I completely blended in with the crowd. After awhile, I started to walk back to Ipanema Beach. Everything looked pretty much the same in Copacabana, considering that I hadn't been there in well over four years. I did enjoy my walk and the beautiful sights along the way.

Once back in Ipanema, I stopped and ate lunch and then I walked down to the beach to think about my "approach" with regard to Therezinha. Since I couldn't talk to her in her own language, it made things very difficult. But no matter. The language barrier was not going to discourage me from pursuing her. Where there is a will, there is a way. I decided to ask Claudio to translate for me. Claudio and I had started to become good friends. I really liked him, and I knew that he understood how much I cared for Therezinha. Claudio also liked Therezinha and wanted to help her.

Before I knew it, it was time to get ready for the evening.

John arrived at the hotel with his wife Celia, and Therezinha, Denise and Ana were in the taxi. We decided to go get something to eat before we went dancing, and we stopped at a little sidewalk cafe in Copacabana. It was now early evening, and the crowds had definitely increased along the beach front. There were women out in force. We ordered some chicken and french fries and drinks. The chicken was delicious. After we finished our dinner, we got into the cab and drove to Scalla's, the same club that held the Red and Black Ball during Carnival 1988. We went inside and heard disco and Brazilian music. We got a table upstairs and sat down. Then we began to talk. Once again, Ana translated for me. The music sounded good and I asked Therezinha to dance. We walked down the stairs to the dance floor. The floor was packed with couples dancing. I was barely able to move. Therezinha began to dance. She was a much better dancer than I. I didn't care; I completely enjoyed watching her dance as she moved her hips from side to side. Therezinha had a beautiful figure. No doubt about it!

We danced until we tired ourselves out, and then we went back upstairs to our table to rest. We ordered more drinks and relaxed. Then the people upstairs next to us began to dance. I also noticed that it had started to get crowded, even on the second level. But everybody seemed to be enjoying themselves. I danced with Denise and Celia and had a great time. I wanted to make sure that they were also enjoying themselves. But, more than anything, I wanted to slow-dance with Therezinha and hold her in my arms, close to my body. However, the DJ did not slow the beat down. It was either disco or Brazilian Samba music over and over. After a few hours we decided to go. Everyone was tired. Once back at the hotel, I kissed Therezinha good night. She told Ana to tell me that tomorrow we would go over to Claudio and Selma's house. I said okay, I'd see her tomorrow.

Tomorrow I had to talk with her about my situation and how I felt about her. I wasn't sure just how she felt about me and I needed to know. I really did.

Chapter
Eight

Around 10:00AM the next morning, the phone rang. It was Therezinha saying good morning and that John would come at noon. When John came, we left for Claudio and Selma's apartment. John dropped me off and then went to get Therezinha. Claudio and I began to talk. He asked if I would like to go to the Rio Zoo. I thought it was a great idea. Then I asked him to translate some things for me once Therezinha arrived, and he said that he would be glad to do that for me.

When Therezinha arrived, we all sat down at the table. Therezinha was on one side, and I was on the other, with Claudio in the middle. I told her that I was filing for a divorce, and it was going to take some time for my lawyer to complete the process. Therezinha didn't say much; she just listened. I also asked her if she wanted to come to California to learn English at a college close to where I lived. She said she would try once again to get a visa so that she could visit and learn English. To acquire even a visitor's visa was a difficult task, I knew. It was not going to be easy. I told Claudio to tell her that I would do my best to help her get out of the country this time. Therezinha said that she would like to come in October, when she would be able to schedule a vacation at work. I told her that October would be okay with me. Then we had a chance to discuss some issues and to clear our thoughts with one another. Claudio did a wonderful job of translating. He was very understanding and kind.

After we talked, we called for a cab and went to the Rio Zoo. It was the largest zoo I had ever seen. It was filled with all kinds of exotic birds and monkeys, all types of animals, and there were a lot of open stretches of green grass for picnickers or for those who wanted to just sit and relax. We walked around and took pictures for the rest of the afternoon.

Tomorrow I was leaving Brazil. The only thing left was to help Therezinha get a visa so that she could come.

It was getting dark, so we went back to Claudio's house for dinner. Selma cooked a wonderful meal for us. After dinner, we talked some more. Then we sang while Claudio played his guitar. Just being next to Therezinha excited me. My feelings were very strong. We got along well, I thought, considering that these were the first days when we had actually spent some time together. We communicated with each other at times by just looking into each other's eyes, and without saying a word, we knew what the other person was thinking or feeling. It was good to see her happy and smiling.

It was time to go and I thanked Claudio and Selma for everything and said good night. John would take Therezinha home, and tomorrow she would ride to the airport with me. I had to get back to work and try to get my business organized for the coming school year, which was fast approaching. I felt good about Therezinha and myself as a couple. This vacation had been necessary. We needed the opportunity to feel one another out and become comfortable with each other.

I got ready for bed. So much had happened in the four and a half years since my last visit—starting with the fact that I had gotten married and was now getting divorced. Anyway, that was the past, and this was the beginning of my future.

After breakfast the next morning, I started to pack. I had gotten used to Ipanema Beach and was going to miss it. The phone rang. It was Therezinha. She said, good morning and that John was on his way. "Okay," I said, and hung up the phone. It didn't take me long to finish packing. John came shortly afterwards. We left to pick up Therezinha. At that time, I thanked her family and told them that I was happy that I had had a chance to meet them. They said they also enjoyed my visit. We left Therezinha's house and went to pick up Claudio and Selma at their apartment, and then we went to the airport.

There was a little bit of time before my flight, so we decided to get something to eat and talk for one last time. Claudio asked Therezinha if there was anything else she wanted to ask me. She said that she was happy that I had come to visit her and she was looking forward to coming to California in October. I gave her some jewelry I had bought for her from Ana. Ana makes jewelry—earrings, necklaces, bracelets. She is very artistic. Therezinha liked my gift, a necklace and pair of earrings, very much. We took some pictures and then it was time to go. I said goodbye to Claudio and Selma. I paid John for his taxi services and thanked him. I liked John, he was a very nice guy and a good driver too. I kissed Therezinha goodbye and left to board the plane.

As I nestled into my seat, I began to think about the trip and what had happened between Therezinha and me. We had gotten to know each other a little better, and that in and of itself made the trip worthwhile. I only wished that we could have spent more time together alone. As the plane taxied on the runway, I smiled.

Now back in San Francisco, I started to get things in order. Summer was ending, and I was anxious to start the school year. Once the school year started and the drivers received their schedules, I was able to concentrate on new contracts for the business. At the same time, I tried to solve other business problems. Therezinha would be in San Francisco next month. I had made arrangements at the college for her to stay in a dormitory, and I would come every day to check on her and to escort her to the many places I wanted her to see. The college enrolls students from all over the world who want to learn English. In this international atmosphere, I knew Therezinha would feel comfortable. She could share similar experiences with others who were also new to the country. She would feel comfortable.

A week later, Therezinha was expecting a call from me at Claudio and Selma's apartment. I called and spoke with Claudio. Therezinha was there, and she told Claudio that she was not able to come. She was denied a visa again. She was very disappointed. She really did want to come. The visa was the problem.

I told Claudio that I would try to help her acquire a visa by another route and to call back next week. I said goodbye to Claudio and hung up the phone. The next day I called the Immigration Office and asked for an explanation of the process to acquire a fiancée visa. They sent me some forms. I realized the only way Therezinha would be able to come to California would be by acquiring a fiancée visa.

Once she was granted a visa, we would have ninety days to marry or she would have to go back to Brazil.

The day had come for me to call her back. Claudio answered the phone. I explained the situation. He understood and explained the situation to Therezinha while I waited. I wasn't sure what her reaction would be to this turn of events. Finally, Claudio got back on the phone and explained that Therezinha understood that she would travel to California using a fiancée visa. Now I knew she would come! We wouldn't necessarily be married in ninety days, but nonetheless, she could enjoy herself and learn English for three months. On the other hand, Therezinha had a job, and she would have to quit her job in order to come out to California. And when she returned to Brazil, she would then have to look for another job. That was a tough decision for her to make, especially since good jobs were hard to find in her country. Finally, I told Claudio that I would return to Brazil in December for Christmas, and we would discuss the whole situation in person. Therezinha liked this idea very much. For myself, I looked forward to seeing her again.

The next few months passed quickly. I received a letter from Therezinha. I opened it. She wrote that things had changed in her life, and she was unsure of what she wanted. And our plans were not to be the same anymore. I was very confused by the letter. Essentially, it seemed that she was telling me not to expect anything from her. I was concerned and ready to go back to Brazil. By now, I had planned to spend Christmas there. No matter what, I wanted to find out what had happened with regard to her feelings for me.

A week later school was out and it was time to go to Brazil. Throughout the entire flight, I thought about her letter. What was going on? What was she trying to tell me in the letter?

It didn't even seem like an eight-hour flight. I guess I was getting used to it. When we landed, I got off the plane and headed out of the airport. There was a crowd, as usual, waiting for the plane. Therezinha was there, along with Claudio and Selma. It was good to see them. Everyone looked fine. Therezinha seemed happy to see me, but there was something uneasy about the situation and I couldn't discern the cause. Whatever it was, I would find out eventually. We left the airport. John drove us once again, and it was good to see him. Therezinha had made reservations for me at the Ipanema Inn Hotel. It was a smaller hotel but in the same excellent location as the Everest Park Hotel, where I had stayed during my last visit. The Ipanema Inn was less expensive and the hotel management just as friendly.

After I checked in, we left for Therezinha's sister's house. At the house, I greeted her father and mother, also her sisters and brothers. Everyone was there, relaxing and talking. It was good to see them again. Everybody was doing well.

The month of December shows a change of season in Brazil, and, true to the season, it was a nice hot day. I sat outside at the back of the house with Claudio. We talked about places to visit, and I told him that I would like to visit São Paulo, which is about forty-five minutes by plane or six hours by bus from Rio. São Paulo was the industrial capital of Brazil. Also, most of the banking business in Brazil is conducted in São Paulo. Claudio warned me that it was very smoggy in São Paulo, just like Los Angeles. He said that he would like to take the trip and show Therezinha and me the city. I told Claudio to ask Therezinha if she would like to go to São Paulo with me. He called Therezinha over and asked her if she would like to go on the trip. She said she would and we planned to go on Christmas Day. Therezinha had never been to São Paulo, so she would have a chance to visit another part of her country. I was excited that she accepted the invitation because I wasn't sure whether or not she would. At the time, I didn't know what she was thinking or feeling about me; I remembered the letter I received from her before I left. One thing I knew, she still cared for me. I could see that in her eyes when she looked at me.

After spending some time with Claudio and with Therezinha's family, I was beginning to feel jet lag, and I was ready to go back to the hotel. John came. I thanked Therezinha and her family for such a nice visit. Claudio, Selma, Therezinha and I left. John dropped off Claudio and Selma at their apartment, and I told Claudio that I would call him later in the week. Therezinha rode back to the hotel with me. Once there, I kissed her goodbye. She looked so beautiful! I wished that she could stay the night.

It was Sunday and Claudio told me before he left that Therezinha would come by on Tuesday, and we would go over to his house for dinner. At dinner, we would talk about our São Paulo trip in more detail. Therezinha was scheduled to work every day; she told Claudio that it was a very busy time at her workplace. At this point, I really didn't care. I was just happy that she was going to São Paulo and that we would spend some more time together.

I woke up fairly well-rested. The bed wasn't as comfortable as the bed in the other hotel, but it would do. The hotel served breakfast, but I went next door to the Everest Park for breakfast. It felt good to be back at Ipanema Beach. I walked down to the beach. It was a beautiful day, so I sat down and looked around. I always enjoyed spending time at the beach. After sitting for awhile, I began to take some pictures. My friends in California wanted me to take more pictures of the women in Brazil. I could understand that! They were truly beautiful!

I decided to go to a movie. The movie was in Portuguese with Italian subtitles. I didn't understand a thing. After the movie, I went to a little restaurant and had lunch. Then I decided to go back to the hotel until dinner time. About four hours or so later, I went to dinner and had a big fish dinner. The Brazilian seafood dinners are very good. After dinner, I walked off the food and noticed that there were a lot of homeless people on the streets. There seemed to be more homeless this time than before. It was almost Christmas, and I started to hand out money to people. They looked up at me and smiled. I wasn't trying to be a saint or anything, but people don't seem to realize how well off they are until they see others who have nothing, and are living in the streets in cardboard boxes. I felt good about the deed that I had done. I just wished that I could have done more.

Tomorrow was Tuesday and I would see Therezinha.

Chapter
Nine

It was the beginning of summer in Brazil, and every day was hot. I could see the beach from my room. The beach was filled with beautiful women. The phone rang. It was Claudio. He said that John would pick me up at 5:00PM and bring me to his apartment. I had to speak frankly with Claudio this evening. He had to know what it was that I wanted to say to Therezinha. I wanted to marry Therezinha and spend the rest of my life with her, and do all that I could for her, if she would have me. The fiancée visa was one way of getting her out of her country to California to visit me. But I wanted more, and she wasn't sure what she wanted anymore. I had to ask her. I had to hear what she would say. I stayed in my hotel room until it was time to leave for the evening. Tonight, I would tell her these things. Tonight I would ask her to marry me. John came and Therezinha was with him. We left and went to Claudio and Selma's apartment.

After dinner we decided to talk. Claudio was ready to translate our conversation. We had decided to spend Christmas weekend in São

Paulo and to take a bus from Rio. We would also rent a car in São Paulo, and Claudio would drive. Of course, Claudio and I would share a room and Selma and Therezinha would do the same.

I then asked Claudio to ask Therezinha the big question. Would she marry me? I didn't want her answer right away—I wanted her to think about it and let me know what her answer was on New Year's Eve. She seemed a little surprised. She said that she would think about it and let me know. She had invited us to her parents' house for a New Year's Eve celebration. We would all be together that evening. Regardless of her answer, she would have to make a decision in the next week.

About an hour later, John arrived and we said goodbye to Claudio and Selma. I thanked them for everything and we left. John took Therezinha home, then drove me back to the hotel. I thought to myself, 'Well I have asked her to marry me. Now I have to wait for her answer.' Waiting was not going to be easy for me, but I didn't want to rush her.

I looked forward to the São Paulo trip on Christmas Day, which would be Friday. A change of scenery would help me relax during my wait. Therezinha was working hard at her job, I could tell. When I saw her at Claudio's the night before, she looked very tired. She said that sometimes she would have to work until nine or ten at night. I felt sorry for her; she worked for pennies on the dollar. She was a dedicated worker. There was nothing I could do to help her in her job, but I could at least give her something to look forward to. A trip to São Paulo, hopefully, would give Therezinha a chance to relax a little and enjoy the new sights.

After dinner I returned to the hotel to watch some TV. The music videos were the only shows I could understand, and they helped me get to sleep at night.

The phone rang the next morning. It was Claudio calling to see how I was doing. Therezinha had asked him to call me this morning and ask me to come over to her parents' house for dinner. It was Christmas Eve. We agreed that John would pick me up around 7:00PM. Claudio then said that he and Selma would meet me at Therezinha's house. I would see them both tonight. After breakfast, I returned to the hotel and paid my bill for the week; I was leaving in the morning, early, around 6:30AM.

I returned to my room and started to pack. I had to get ready for the trip to São Paulo and get ready to check out of the hotel. I had only one suitcase and one carry-on bag. I put the clothes for São Paulo in my carry-on and the rest in my suitcase. One thing I learned about traveling internationally is to dress light and take carry-on suitcases and bags only. Saves a lot of time and trouble.

I finished my packing and was ready to leave in the morning. Before long, John came to the hotel, and we left for Therezinha's parents' home.

Once we arrived, we saw the house filled with people. Most everyone was a family member. Some I had met before and some I hadn't. Claudio and Selma were there also, and everybody seemed to be celebrating the eve of Christmas. I had bought a dozen roses for Therezinha and my gift seemed to make her happy. She got a vase and placed the roses in water. Family members were eating and talking and listening to music. Therezinha and I sat on the couch. I asked Claudio to take a picture of the two of us. After that, we began to take pictures of her family with my camera—her brothers and sisters, mother and father, uncles and aunts, Claudio and Selma, everybody. I was having a great time. As far as I could tell, Therezinha looked happy after the picture-taking. Claudio and I talked for awhile. I said that I was ready to go to São Paulo. He said that he and Selma were also ready. I wanted to get some rest before we left for our trip, and I wanted to go. I thanked Therezinha and her parents for inviting me to the party and said good night. Even though I wasn't home, I could feel that Christmas was in the air in Rio de Janeiro.

I asked the man at the front desk to schedule a wake-up call for me at 6:00AM. The next thing I remember, the phone was ringing next to the bed. It was Christmas Day. John was at the hotel at 6:30AM and we left to get Claudio and Selma. We picked them up and then went to Therezinha's house. I had a Christmas present for her, a jewelry music box. She was happy with the gift. It was now time to go to the bus station to catch the bus to São Paulo. We arrived there and it was crowded with people trying to travel across Rio on Christmas Day. The station was bustling. There was a constant flow of buses of all shapes and sizes trying to enter the station to pick up passengers. Claudio bought all of our tickets, and after about forty-five minutes, we boarded the bus. Our bus was very nice and well-equipped. It had air-conditioning, tinted glass, reclining seats and all the modern amenities. I was quite impressed. The bus soon filled with passengers, and the driver loaded the luggage space under the bus. Finally, we were ready to leave. Claudio's and Selma's seats were in front of Therezinha and me, so we were able to talk on the way to São Paulo. Claudio said it would take about six hours to get to São Paulo.

The day was beautiful, so the road would be clear. São Paulo is located inland, whereas Rio practically sits on the water. Also, São

Paulo is located in the mountains and is much colder than Rio. On the way, Claudio told us that we would have to climb a hillside, and then the road would begin to level out.

Therezinha sat by the window and looked out at the mountain scenery as the bus began to slowly climb. Claudio and I talked about the itinerary once we arrived in São Paulo. We would find a hotel and rent a car. I was enjoying myself tremendously. It was always a pleasure to talk with Claudio. I was very happy that he and Selma were able to take the trip; otherwise, Therezinha and I would not have been able to go. I appreciated Claudio's friendship.

The ride to São Paulo provided extraordinary scenery. We saw lush green pastures and farm animals grazing lazily on the hillsides. Small and large farms and country homes peppered the hillsides. The land was truly beautiful.

Claudio and I continued to talk. After awhile, I looked over at Therezinha. She had fallen asleep, and her face gently lay against the bus window. A reflection of sunlight off the bus window passed over her face, and to me she looked like a Sleeping Beauty. She slept so gently that I could not even hear her breathe. I didn't want to wake her. She was the only woman I knew who looked as beautiful when asleep as when awake.

After awhile, Therezinha woke up and smiled. She seemed happy and seemed to be enjoying the ride.

More time passed, and then Claudio said that we had about one more hour of travel before we would reach São Paulo. It started to get a little dark, twilight, and the sun was setting. I fell asleep.

The next thing I remember was Claudio saying to me, "Welcome to São Paulo, my brother!"

Chapter
Ten

Once off the bus, we took another bus to the airport. We could rent a car there. Then we drove to the Excelsior Hotel in downtown São Paulo. A McDonald's restaurant, an interesting sight for an American, was next to the hotel. The city teemed with people of all nationalities, walking and talking and celebrating the holiday. Our hotel rooms were very nice. We had asked for adjoining rooms so that we could talk to one another without having to go in the hallway to knock at the door.

We settled in, showered and dressed for dinner. We left the hotel to look for a restaurant. Claudio mentioned that there were all kinds of restaurants offering all nationalities of food in São Paulo. He assured us that we could find any kind of food we could imagine. Eventually, we decided to have dinner at a little restaurant that specialized in steak, a South American steakhouse. We went inside and ordered dinner. Claudio had friends living in São Paulo, so after dinner we decided to visit his friends. We drove to their home for a visit. They were very nice, and I even managed to talk with them with Claudio's help. Then we all agreed to go out on the town and see a Samba show.

Before we knew it, there were about ten of us walking down the city street, laughing and talking. We went into a club, and luckily the show was just about to begin. We ordered drinks at our table, one of many tables lined up in a row across the huge dance floor. The show started and the Samba dancers came out one by one, shaking their butts as only Samba dancers can. It always amazes me how Brazilian girls move so well when they dance and how they shake their hips effortlessly. My eyes were glued to the stage. It was very entertaining, and the drummers were absolutely outstanding. After the show, we ordered some food at the table. Everybody seemed to be having a great time. Therezinha and I and Claudio and Selma got up and went to the dance floor and started dancing. Therezinha showed me how to do the Samba. I was trying to follow her as she moved her hips around the dance floor. After awhile, we returned to the table.

Then a gay comedian came on stage. The audience laughed out loud at each joke, but I didn't understand a word. At the close of his act, the comedian pulled out a Brazilian flag, and the audience began to chant, "Brazil! Brazil! Brazil!" I realized that no matter what the country, people love their homeland. After an hour or so, we left. I had really enjoyed my first evening in São Paulo!

We drove back to the hotel. It had been a long, long day. Claudio said good night to Selma, and I said good night to Therezinha.

The next morning greeted us with a brilliant sunshine. Claudio and I got up and took our turns in the shower. While I waited for him to finish in the bathroom, I could hear Therezinha and Selma in the next room. When Claudio came out, I asked him to check on them and to see when they would be ready for breakfast. I took my shower, and when I came out, Claudio said that they would meet me in the dining room. About ten minutes later, I met them there. They were eating and talking. I said good morning to Therezinha and Selma, and I ordered some breakfast. We decided to do some shopping, drive around the city and take pictures. Claudio had brought his 35mm camera, which takes beautiful pictures. We would get double prints of the pictures.

During breakfast, Therezinha didn't say much to me. Actually, she had been rather quiet the previous evening. She had a lot on her mind, I was sure, after my proposal to her. We slowly finished breakfast and went off to shop.

São Paulo has some beautiful shopping centers with everything imaginable in them—all first-class merchandise. We walked around one mall and took pictures of one another and just enjoyed the shops. We left the shopping center within the hour because Claudio wanted to show me the city museum. We visited the museum and saw snakes, birds and bone fossils. I liked walking around the rooms and stopping at displays that showed ancient birds and animals. Of course, we took pictures. After awhile, we left to find our car. We didn't want to stay in one place for very long since we were leaving the next day. We kept up a good pace and moved from place to place. Selma's aunt and uncle lived in São Paulo, so we went to visit them. As with every single family I had ever met in Brazil, they too were warm and very kind.

Before we knew it, the day was over. It was now time for dinner. We went to a restaurant a few blocks from our hotel. After dinner, we drove around town some more, and then we finally went back to our hotel. We ended up talking most of the night with one another.

Then Therezinha and Selma returned to their room.

The Christmas weekend had passed so quickly! I rose early, and Claudio was already up and dressed. Soon Therezinha and Selma were also ready, and we went to breakfast together. We had planned to leave that afternoon, so Claudio suggested that we quickly walk to a flea market not too far from the hotel right after we pack. We could still visit one more place before we left.

After breakfast we went to our rooms to pack our clothes. It took only twenty minutes and everybody was finished. We checked out of the hotel and walked to the flea market down the street.

We walked around the booths of the vendors, each vendor displaying a lot of different things. It was interesting to me to just walk around and look at the people as they tried to make deals either buying or selling merchandise. We stayed there for about an hour or so, then decided to take our rental car back to the airport. After we returned the car, we took the city bus back to the bus station, which was as crowded as before, with people now trying to get back to their home towns after Christmas.

Finally, our bus came and we boarded. We were headed back to Rio de Janeiro. Claudio and I talked, and I asked him if he would remind Therezinha that I had to have my answer on New Year's Eve, which was just three days away. Claudio then turned to Therezinha and told her what I had just said. She said she understood and would have an answer for me. I still couldn't tell what she was thinking, but I could tell that she had enjoyed São Paulo, and I had certainly enjoyed being around her.

After about an hour, Claudio and I stopped talking. Therezinha had fallen asleep and so had Selma. So, I decided to sleep too. The return trip always seems much longer to me. It began to rain, and the road was a little rough. The bus driver had to drive slowly in order to control the bus. We had our usual rest stops along the way, and finally we arrived in Rio. We were all very, very tired. Therezinha called John and asked him to pick us up. He drove to Claudio and Selma's house and dropped them off. I thanked Claudio for the whole weekend. He said that he enjoyed the trip and so did Selma.

John took me to the hotel. Therezinha thanked me for taking her to São Paulo. I told her I was happy I could do that for her. I kissed her and said, "See ya at the New Year's Eve party."

Now, all I needed was a "Yes" from Therezinha and I would be a very happy man. I slept unusually well, considering that when I travel I am a light sleeper. By now I was bored with Ipanema Beach; I had walked around enough times to see everything there was to see. Probably I was just anxious. I wanted to get my answer from Therezinha. Night time arrived. The day was over. Only two days to go before I would know her reply.

The next morning the phone rang loudly. It was Claudio. He said that tomorrow he would like me to stay at his house and to come about noon. He would call John and arrange my transport. Claudio was only going to work for half a day, since it was New Year's Eve. I was glad that I would be leaving my hotel room tomorrow.

I did a lot of thinking that day about Therezinha and what her answer might be. If she said "No," I had to accept it and move on.

I decided that I had to take a walk. I noticed that the weather cools off at night. On the beach there is a constant breeze that comes off the South Atlantic, and it helps you sleep when it is so hot you can hardly breath. I tried to keep positive thoughts in my mind and hoped that everything would turn out well…

The next morning I paid my bill and waited for John to arrive and we left. It was a very hot day, especially inland, where there was no breeze. Claudio was home and Selma too. Selma's sister, Sonya, was there also. She was visiting from Timbaúba, which is the northeast part of Brazil. They sat around and chatted, and Claudio talked about how hot it was in Rio de Janeiro and how it was going to get even hotter in January. Then we left to go to the store. Selma had to do some shopping and run some errands. We returned a few hours later, and I decided to take a nap. I wanted to be well-rested for the party that night.

About two hours later, Claudio knocked on the bedroom door.

"Time to get up."

I woke up, got dressed and found myself as ready as I could be. Claudio called Therezinha to tell her that we were coming over. She said the party was going to be held at her sister's house, right around the corner from her parents' home. She told Claudio that she would send John over to pick us up. John arrived shortly and we all left for the party.

It took only about fifteen minutes to get there. Everyone was dancing and drinking and having a good time. After all, it was New Year's Eve. Therezinha's mother fixed me a big plate of food. It was excellent. I saw Therezinha, and she looked very pretty. She wore a nice-looking dress that hugged her lovely figure. I was looking at her face trying to read it for my answer. I still could not tell!

Everyone was taking pictures and celebrating the old year out and the new year in. Marcia came over with her husband Marcos. I hadn't met her before, personally. It was really a pleasure to meet her, finally. She had been just as much a part of our long-distance relationship over these past years. We talked for awhile. Finally, it was midnight. The music stopped playing and we gathered around in a circle. Therezinha's father said a prayer thanking God for the new year and asking that He keep everybody safe from hurt and from harm and from pain. I was very touched by the closeness of her family. After the prayer, everybody toasted in the New Year, 1993. Firecrackers were beginning to light up the sky all over Rio de Janeiro. It was an experience for me to see how Brazilians ring in the new year. And they certainly celebrate!

The time had come for Therezinha's answer. Claudio called Therezinha over to him and said, "Let's go for a walk."

All three of us left the house by way of the back yard. We walked down the sidewalk. Claudio then asked Therezinha for her answer, and she told him. She talked with him for a minute or two.

Claudio turned to me and I could tell the answer by the look on his face. He told me that her answer was "No." I asked, "Why?" Claudio said that Therezinha was expecting a promotion from her job and that she wasn't sure about leaving her family and friends and traveling to a foreign country. She couldn't speak English and California was so far away. Claudio continued Therezinha's comments that I was a very special person in her life and always would be. We returned to the party. Everybody was still enjoying themselves. The fireworks lit up the sky, and the party-goers were still celebrating, now even more loudly. I stayed for awhile and did my best to enjoy the party. But I was tired. It was now about 2:00AM. It was still hot outside. I was ready for bed.

I was very disappointed with her answer, but at least I knew where I stood. John came to take us back to Claudio and Selma's. Before the three of us left, I thanked everybody for inviting me and said good night. On the drive back, Claudio said that he had hoped that Therezinha's answer would have been "Yes."

"Me too," I said softly.

Once back at Claudio and Selma's, I spoke again. "Thank you for your help. Happy New Year and good night."

It took a long time for me to fall asleep; it was very hot and I was filled with emotions. I lay in the bed for awhile, trying to get sleepy. It was now Saturday and I would be leaving the next day. My mind was trying to shift back to my work and my business. It was a new year and I wanted to make some changes with the business in order to improve it. Truthfully, I forced myself to think about work in order to keep my mind off Therezinha.

Claudio knocked on the door.

"Come in."

"Good morning, how are you?"

I said, "Hot."

Claudio and Selma had friends they wanted to visit that morning, and they were not too far away.

"No problem, I would like to go with you," I answered. "Okay, I hoped you would."

We left after breakfast.

Claudio's son had come over, Claudio Jr., and he joined us for the day. We stayed at their friend's house for most of the day and evening. They were a nice family.

We finally returned to Claudio's house and watched TV and talked. The phone rang. It was Therezinha asking what time I had planned to leave tomorrow. Claudio told her. She said that she would go to the airport with me.

It was still hot, and I knew it was going to be a long night. It seemed like an eternity.

Claudio woke me up in the morning. I heard him talking in the living room. I asked Claudio if we could develop the pictures we had taken of our trip to São Paulo and the party at Therezinha's sister's house. He said we could, right after breakfast.

We walked to the film store. The clerk said that it would take about four hours to develop the film. When we went back to the house, Claudio's daughter Andrea had come over to visit.

I was just waiting, waiting for the time to pass. Claudio went to pick up the pictures and returned shortly after. The photos turned out very well. I got my prints and put them in my suitcase. Then Therezinha arrived with John. She wanted to see the pictures we had taken. She seemed to like them.

We left for the airport. John parked the taxi, and I checked in at the counter. When I was finished, I went over to where they were sitting. I paid John and thanked Claudio, Selma and John for everything. I said goodbye to Therezinha and went to board the plane. I turned back to look at Therezinha one last time. There would be no reason for me to come back to Rio de Janeiro. She had been my only reason.

I was in a daze. The next thing I remember was hearing someone say, "Your passport, please."

Chapter
Eleven

I knew that it would be a long, eight-hour flight. I sat in my seat, looking straight ahead, in a very crowded plane. A lot of people came to Rio to get away from the winter in the States. I noticed a guy who sat across from me on my left. As he looked for something in his carry-on, he pulled out his passport, and I noticed that he was an American. His complexion was fair, and I thought that he could have been Brazilian.

His said that his name was Hyatt, he was a physician and he had traveled from his home on the East Coast. We began to talk further, and after several minutes, he came over and sat down next to me. Hyatt had visited Brazil to enjoy the good weather. I told him about Therezinha, how I had visited her and her family for the holidays. And I told him that I had asked Therezinha to marry me and she had said "No." Chatting with Hyatt had cheered me up a little. Still, my mind focused on my disappointment, and one part of me said, 'Go back to the drawing board,' and another part of me said, 'Move on, it's easier that way…'

We talked about some of the places in Rio and nearby Rio where we had visited, and I learned that Hyatt had done quite a bit of traveling himself. I told him that if he wanted to meet some good-looking women, he might want to visit the Dominican Republic. Hyatt then asked me if I would want to go with him to the Dominican Republic some time in the future; I could show him around the island. 'Why not?' I thought. Therezinha was not a part of my life anymore, and I had to find another woman to marry. My chances of finding a beautiful woman and beginning a relationship were good in the Dominican Republic. Why waste time? For the next hour of the flight, we made plans to leave for the Dominican Republic in the summer, during July.

Hyatt told me what a good time he had had in Brazil. It was his second trip that year. Mine also. After a little more general conversation, we stopped talking. I fell into a deep sleep, and I woke to the voice of the pilot saying, "Buckle your seat belts and prepare for landing in Miami International." It was about 5:00AM when we landed. I was tired. Hyatt and I walked through Customs, and we both passed through with no problem. There wasn't a long line of people that early in the morning. We decided to have a little breakfast and continue to talk for awhile. Hyatt had never been to the West and I never been to the East of our own continent, but we both had been to a lot of places outside of the United States. Soon it was time for us to catch our planes to our destinations. We said our goodbyes and left for different gates.

I slept on the plane on the way back to San Francisco. As I walked up the ramp and into the airport, I realized how very tired I was, mentally and physically. California was cold compared to Rio de Janeiro. School would be starting again. When I got home, I unpacked, took a long, hot shower and slipped into bed. It felt good to be back home and to be sleeping in my own bed. But it was a lonely bed, with just me in it.

School started the next day. I didn't want to get up, but I had to. The children were waiting for me. I went to the school bus at 6:30 in the morning. I cranked open the bus door, and as I entered, I felt as if I was walking into a refrigerator. The first day back passed pretty fast, once I got out there on the road with the children. After school, I went to my office and started working on some of my paperwork. I wanted to get everything in order for the new year.

Before I knew it, January had passed. Therezinha's birthday had come. Before I had left Rio, I bought a birthday card for her and asked Claudio to give it to her on her birthday. I decided to call Claudio. He told me that he had given Therezinha the card and that she liked it. We talked for a few minutes. Claudio said that he and Selma were doing fine. He repeated that it was good to hear from me.

For the next four months, all I did was work and return home. I only did what I had to do, and nothing extra. I didn't hustle for extra work as usual. If a school called to schedule a field trip, I would schedule the trip. If a school didn't call, I didn't care. This was out of character for me, because ever since I was a little boy I always hustled for money. Nobody had ever given me anything. Once, when I was about fourteen or fifteen, I asked my father for a motorcycle. He said, "If you want it, get a job and buy it yourself." So I did. I got a paper route, saved my money and bought a motorcycle—and I appreciated it more than if he had bought it for me.

I knew that I was in a rut. Therezinha had not left my mind. My only consolation was that she knew that I had at least made an effort to be with her, and even though we were on separate paths, I was grateful for the opportunity to reach into the past for something that I truly wanted.

When a person tries to reach back into the past for something or someone, often that person is not there or has made another choice. Even though I didn't get the answer I wanted, I realized that Therezinha cared for me. I saw that. I saw it in her eyes, and the eyes don't lie. Well, at least I had had a chance to see her again and to meet her family and to spend time with her. That experience alone was worth the trip.

June came, and by now I hadn't written to Therezinha in six months. My friend Hyatt called to discuss our upcoming trip to the Dominican Republic. Another friend of mine, Tony, would join us on the trip. Tony lived in San Francisco and also planned to take his vacation in July, so I invited him to come along. Besides, Tony had seen my pictures of the beautiful women in the Dominican Republic, and he knew what to expect. While making my long-distance calls and setting a travel itinerary, I also wrote a letter to Therezinha. I told her that I was going to Fort Lauderdale to visit my family, and from there to the Caribbean. I wrote that I hoped she was doing well.

About a week later, school was out for the summer. I had a busy summer schedule lined up and had to hire extra drivers to cover all of the summer trips. It was now July and it was time to go.

Tony and I flew to Miami and met Hyatt at Miami International. Then the three of us left for the Dominican Republic.

We landed and went through Customs. It was hot there as usual. It felt good to be back in the Dominican. The Dominican Republic is on the island of Hispaniola and borders Haiti to the north.

The Dominican Republic possesses two-thirds of the island and Haiti the other third. The three of us left the airport, stuffed ourselves into a small taxi and went to our hotel. We had made reservations at a hotel located by the *malacon*, which means "area by the water." During the evenings, tourists as well as locals go down to the *malacon* to eat and drink, and to dance and relax. This seaside area is where everyone hangs out, and there are lots of women around the *malacon*.

Tony and Hyatt began to hang out together, walking around and taking in the sights. I laughed when I saw them; they looked as if their eyes were going to pop out of their heads! It was funny to look at their spontaneous reactions as the women passed by them. I must admit that I probably looked just like them on my first trip to the Dominican…

A major tourist street called LaConde cuts through the city, and LaConde is where throngs of vacationers shop and tour. It is always a very busy street, packed on both sides. I like to sit at one of the outdoor cafes on LaConde Street and watch the women go by and smile at the ones I liked. We went down to LaConde Street, leisurely strolling past the shops. We decided to stop at a cafe and order something to eat. It was hot on our first day. After awhile, I decided to go back to the hotel to relax. I hadn't seen any woman in particular I wished to engage in conversation. Tony and Hyatt decided to stay on LaConde. No problem. They knew how to get back by to the hotel by themselves. I had to get out of the sun!

Once back, I showered and relaxed. About four hours had passed, and I decided to get something to eat at the hotel. Tony and Hyatt still hadn't returned. After dinner, I walked down by the *malacon*, and I found them sitting in a little bar-restaurant, still enjoying the sights. I told them that I wanted to take a walk and would catch up with them later.

I walked farther down the beach front and then stopped. I walked out on the beach and sat down by the water and listened to Merengue music that was playing in the distance. Merengue music has a fast, compelling beat. It felt good to be on vacation. Even though I had planned to actively look for a special woman on this vacation, a woman I could start a relationship with, still, I wanted to be very careful in choosing. If she didn't have what I want, mentally and physically, I would just move along. And I definitely didn't want a woman who would go to bed with me at first meeting. That was for sure. I was on a mission of sorts, searching for that certain "someone." No doubt about it, the effort was as easy as looking for a needle in a hay stack, but I wasn't going to give up until I found her.

While sitting quietly on the beach, I realized that I was beginning to get a grip on myself. It was time for me to bounce back like only I could. I was ready to accept the past and move on to the future, to where my new happiness would be found. I didn't know where "she" would be found, San Francisco, another country, an island—but I would find her one way or another.

I finally returned to the room. Tony and Hyatt were in the hotel by that time. We reserved three single rooms in a row, close quarters for the "three amigos." I hadn't asked how long they had been there. I must have stayed down by the water longer than I thought. It was very late.

The next morning we got up and went to a restaurant for breakfast. After breakfast, we walk around the town. The Dominican Republic is a friendly island, and it is easy to get along with others. People can party and drink together without fighting or starting trouble. No one bothers anyone else, whether day or night. So, tourists enjoy the vacation spot with the locals without trouble. To the great appreciation of the male tourist, there are at least eight women for every man, and most men seeking company can have his pick, if that's what he wants. For me, if all I wanted was a good time, I didn't have to travel thousands of miles for it. That was not my intention. On vacation, women approached me all of the time, and I said, "*No, gracias.*" I was there for another reason.

After walking for a few hours with Hyatt and Tony, the hot island sun began to get to me; it's amazing how quickly it zaps you and takes your energy away. We started to walk back toward LaConde Street. The street was bustling as usual, with people selling and shopping and walking around, taking in the island atmosphere. Of course, there were some pretty women to see. Tony and Hyatt tried to get used to the situation. I explained to them that a visitor can never get used to all of the beauty. I told them both that if they saw a woman they wanted to pursue, they must be sure that the particular woman was the one they wanted. If, however, they remained uncertain, they would end up drifting from one beautiful woman to another. There was no end to the beauty that surrounded them. My point: Make up your mind and go for it, that is, go for that one particular woman that you may like. They understood what I was saying, I guess. And they knew that I took my own advice.

After about a half an hour, I decided to return to my room, I had enough sights for the day.

Tony and Hyatt stayed downtown. We had planned to all go out to a disco later in the evening. I walked back to the hotel and almost fell out—it had been so hot throughout the entire day. Before I realized it, it was evening. Tony and Hyatt were back, and we showered and dressed for dinner. After dinner we went down to the *malacon* to check out some discos. Several women were standing outside of one particular club. We went in, and the club was crowded with people dancing to American disco and Merengue music. I looked around the large room as I listened to the music. I saw no one who appealed to me; I decided to relax and not pursue anyone. About 1:00AM, I was ready to leave and told Tony and Hyatt that I would go back to the hotel. They said okay, and I left. I walked back to the hotel and got ready for bed. I watched some TV, then fell asleep.

The next morning, I called Tony's room and Hyatt's room to see if they wanted to have breakfast together. They did. At breakfast they said that they had had a good time the night before. After I had left, they went to another disco and danced some more. I was glad they had a good time. It wasn't that I hadn't enjoyed myself, but my mind was set in a different mode. After breakfast, I decided to stay around the hotel and take it easy. The next couple of days passed quickly, as they do when on vacation and having fun.

Tony and I planned to leave, and Hyatt planned to stay a few days longer. Tony flew on to San Francisco, and I went back to Fort Lauderdale to visit my family. I had had a good time in the Dominican Republic. I knew that I would be back soon. Once in Fort Lauderdale, I told my Aunt Carmen about the trip and how much I had enjoyed myself in her country.

All of the family were doing fine. After a few days, I returned to San Francisco. It was time to get back to work. I was happy to have had the chance to get away for a week and relax. I arrived home about midnight. The next day was Sunday. I went to church. After church, I rested all day and got ready for my busy summer schedule. Monday morning arrived. I talked to my drivers, and there were no major problems either with them or the buses.

The summer passed fast. Before I realized it, it was the month of August. Once again, I had a lot of preparation to complete before the next school year. It was a good summer and I enjoyed it very much.

Chapter
Twelve

Therezinha sent me a card, wishing me a happy birthday. I was happy to get a birthday card from her, since I hadn't heard from her in more than eight months. I had wondered how she was doing. In her card, she said she was fine. My mind had drifted back to the last time we were together in Rio de Janeiro. Eventually I would find another beautiful woman to take her place, but she would always play a big part in my romantic memories. I couldn't erase her from my mind completely.

I thought about how things might have been if she had said "Yes" and we were together. We could be happy together, pursuing our life goals and supporting one another, bonded together as one. But in reality, that was not the case.

Her birthday card had set me backwards, and I didn't need that to happen. It had been hard enough for me for the last eight months...

School finally started a week later. The school year began well, and the last four months of the year always go by fast. In the winter months, not much extra work is available. So, I have to make it while I can, and I was ready for the task. I wanted to finish up the year strong. Hyatt called and wanted to spend Thanksgiving in the Dominican Republic. And he wanted me to meet him there. I said okay; the weather would be nice in the Dominican Republic in November and cold in California. I continued to work very hard so that I would have extra money for my vacation expenses.

Finally, November was upon us. And for the second time that year, I left California for the Dominican Republic.

Hyatt had learned his way around the island, better than I, as a matter of fact. He rented a car so that we could drive around and see more of the island. The weather was pleasant, not too hot—perfect weather for November. I planned to stay for about four days, and Hyatt planned for the same amount of time. We would leave on the same day. Back at home, school was out for Thanksgiving vacation. It felt good to relax and not worry about the business for a few days.

The island is very much "Americanized." The Dominican Republic is located west of Puerto Rico, and with such proximity, the Dominicans tend to copy a lot of the American cultural aspects. Besides that, it is a pleasant place to relax and look for women. Since Hyatt decided to rent a car, I decided to split the cost and split the driving with him. It made it much better for the both of us, and we didn't have to do much walking. We drove to the different beaches in the area, parked, and then walked around, looking at the beautiful women and smiling.

The days went by dramatically fast. We both enjoyed ourselves very much, and we had really come to know our way around the island. In addition, Hyatt had learned to speak Espanol! He had just started studying it, but he could communicate very well. We had decided that our next trip would be to Puerto Plata, which is the northeastern part of the country. Puerto Plata is a resort area, and we had heard that it was beautiful. I was ready for a change of scenery and anxious to check it out. We couldn't go wrong visiting Puerto Plata the next time around.

Thanksgiving day arrived. The hotel served a Thanksgiving dinner for their patrons. It was terrible. By the end of the festivities, I was ready to return home and get back to work. The only thing the Thanksgiving dinner did for me was to make me wish I was home having Thanksgiving dinner with my family.

After dinner, I felt a little ill. The next morning came and I packed. Hyatt was also up and ready to go. We left the hotel, went to the airport and turned in the rented car, then departed for Miami. Once in Miami, we said goodbye to one another and promised to keep it touch.

Now back in San Francisco, I had a couple of days to rest before school started again. The weekend passed, and I did manage to get my fill of good holiday food—turkey and dressing and sweet potato pie. You don't realize how much you miss something until you don't have it...

It was now Monday morning and the first day back to school. The weather was getting cold in northern California. Winter was fast approaching—you could feel it in the air. In about three weeks, school would be out for Christmas vacation.

In the first week of December, Hyatt called to see how I had been. He said that he wanted to go to Carnival in Trinidad in February and to Caracas, Venezuela. I said that the Carnival in Trinidad was supposed to be very good. Hyatt continued that he would begin to plan our trip. I had some time off in February from school, so I could arrange to go with him. The last Carnival I had gone to was in Rio de Janeiro, and now I could compare Trinidad's Carnival with Rio's.

The next couple of weeks passed, and school was out for Christmas vacation. I had no plans other than to relax and think about the past year. What a year that had been! But I had managed to get through it, and I even felt good about it. I sent a card to Therezinha wishing her a Merry Christmas and Happy New Year. It had been a full year since I had visited and had asked her to marry me. I hoped she and her family were doing okay. About a week later, I received my Christmas card from Therezinha, wishing me the same greeting.

I enjoyed Christmas with my family. It was good to be home even though it was cold, but that is the way Christmas should be in America. I still hadn't found anyone who was special to me. But I didn't want that to be a reason not to enjoy the holidays, so I didn't think about it. I just looked forward to my trip to Trinidad in February. I knew that it would be exciting and different.

Before long, New Year's Eve 1994 arrived. Wow, the time was moving by fast. I didn't do anything on New Year's Eve—usually I don't. But I remember promising myself that I would have somebody next year at this time. I though, 'How nice it would be to say Happy New Year to the woman you love.'

Therezinha
Well, there was a lot going on during this time. I needed some time
away from the preoccupation of work. I needed some time for myself,
some time to look inward. My emotional side had been forgotten, as I
had tried to improve my situation at work. I wanted to at least get
minimum wages, so that I did not have to depend on anybody. That was
all I was living for at the time. I stopped and thought, 'I am tired of all
of this.' I decided to forget about work for awhile and to think about my
emotional side. I was tired of everything... I was tired of fighting in
court for my labor rights. It was at that time that I stopped and
reflected. I gave myself some private time, and I think I was changing.
I began to realize what I really wanted. I thought I had already found
the right person. I once wrote to Kevin that, unfortunately, we cannot
command our hearts, and if I had to choose I would have chosen him to
marry. I wasn't doing so well at the time. I needed to be sure of what I
wanted. I was getting there... In 1994, things started to change because
I gave myself some time—January, February, March, April...

At the business, I had lots of work to do in order to keep things going
at the level it had now reached. School had started and I was back to
my routine of driving. It was good to be back after two weeks of
doing nothing. I had to be doing something or else I would get
bored. In the winter, when it was cold, my mind would sometimes
drift to thoughts of the Caribbean, where it was warm and pleasant,
and I wished I was there. But I knew I had to take care of business in
California if I wanted to go anywhere else. Business first.

It was mid-January. Hyatt called and said he was getting ready for our
trip. I told him I was doing the same and looked forward to going.
Hyatt was ready, I could tell he was ready to go. I felt the same way.

The days drifted by and it was now the end of January. I sent
Therezinha a birthday card wishing her a happy birthday.

Before I knew it, it was time to go to Trinidad, and I was more than
ready to go. I was excited about going somewhere different. The
language spoken in Trinidad is English; so, I would have no problems
in terms of communication. I met Hyatt at Miami International. It
was good to see him. We talked for awhile, then it was time to catch
the plane to Puerto Rico. We boarded the plane. It took about two
hours to get to Puerto Rico. We took a plane to Barbados from
Puerto Rico, and from there, a plane to Tobago, and from Tobago to
Trinidad. It took more than a few hours, but we finally made it there.
It was night when we arrived. We took a taxi from the airport and
planned to find a hotel. We found that every place was booked, but
we kept looking. Eventually we found a hotel and checked in. It was
about midnight. I said good night to Hyatt and left for my room. I
showered and got into bed and turned off the light.

The next thing I knew, I saw little bugs flying around the room. It
was a "flea-bag" hotel! I got up and turned on the lights. Bugs were
flying everywhere—fleas! I got dressed and left the room. I went to
Hyatt's room to ask him if he had fleas in his room and he said no. I
told him that I was moving out of my room. I went back, collected
my belongings and went to the front desk. I was given another room.

As I slipped underneath the bed covers in my new room, I felt almost
too tired to sleep. Several minutes later, I slowly began to drift off,
with my last thought, 'Wow, what a way to begin a vacation!'

Chapter
Thirteen

Morning came, and I hadn't sleep well at all. I remember waking up and turning on the room light to check for fleas. I didn't see any, but still I had to check the room thoroughly. I went to the breakfast bar. Hyatt was already there, sitting on a stool eating breakfast. I ordered something to eat and sat down. After breakfast, we hailed a taxi and rode around town in order to get our bearings. It was a nice, mildly warm day. We rode around, checking out the sites. I asked the taxi driver to show us where the Carnival celebrations were going to be held. He pointed to a hotel where a big party was planned for that evening. He said that it was going to be one of the better ones.

We returned to the hotel and decided to have lunch and then walk around by ourselves and check out the new surroundings. A lot of people were lunching at the hotel who had arrived from all parts of the world. We met a couple from the Grand Cayman Islands. They had come to Trinidad to enjoy Carnival. A really friendly couple, they told us a little about the Grand Cayman Islands. They said it was a perfect place for snorkeling, since the water is a crystal-clear blue. They added that their homeland is very friendly, and tourists always seem to enjoy themselves. After we talked, they left the hotel. We were right behind them, since we were anxious to explore Trinidad.

As we walked, we saw some very pretty women. We began to look forward to the party that evening. After walking for awhile, we returned to the hotel. The weather had turned a little muggy; I told Hyatt that I was going to take a nap and get ready for the evening. I returned to the room and took a two-hour nap. I got up and washed my face. Then I went to Hyatt's room. He was nearly ready.

I said, "Let's go and eat in town."

"Sounds good!"

We left the hotel by taxi and went downtown. We decided on a little restaurant by the water and ordered some seafood. The restaurant was filled with customers anticipating a fun evening of Carnival. The restaurant staff was fabulous, and the food was excellent. After dinner we returned to the hotel and showered and dressed for the party. We had told the taxi to return in one hour.

The taxi arrived on time and away we went. I wanted to have a good time in Trinidad. It took us about ten minutes to get to the hotel. The hotel was located on the side of a hill, and we saw cars lined up the hill and around the corner. The hotel's parking lot was packed with cars too. Not a single parking space was in sight. I thought to myself, 'I'm glad I'm not driving!'

The taxi dropped us off and we headed toward the hotel. To our surprise, the party was outside and not inside. We walked around the building and down a walkway. It was crowded with people. Finally, we were at the party site, and what a party site it was! A steel band was playing so loudly that it practically pierced the eardrums. A huge swimming pool was in the center of the courtyard, and men and women stood along both sides of the pool. We were able to walk around the party, circling the pool and observing the people and the scenery. The party was packed with lovely women. Many of the women displayed a racial mix, probably Creeb Indian, and they had long, black silky hair and a dark complexion. They were fine. No doubt about it.

I walked around the pool, an Olympic-size pool at that. I looked in amazement. The women were also checking me out. I didn't stop and talk to anyone in particular, I only walked around and looked. I noticed that Hyatt was doing the same. We had split up, and I knew that sooner or later we would bump into one another again. The hotel matched the swimming pool in size—it was absolutely huge. And everyone was partying! Couples and small groups were laughing and drinking and dancing to the sounds of the steel drum band. The Carnival energy made me want to dance.

I stopped walking and began to check out the happenings all around me. I was also watching my back. I was in a foreign country, and you never know what can happen; so, I remained very aware of individuals standing next to me or behind me. Even though I was alert, I wasn't anticipating any trouble, and the atmosphere was comfortable and full of fun.

In about an hour or so, I bumped into Hyatt. He had been dancing and moving from one section of the party to another. And, of course, girl-watching. We both agreed that it was great party. Trinidad at night was spectacular! The sky held a bright, full moon that lit up the pale blue stucco hotel and the grounds, and the pool lights had cast a white-gold glow over the party-goers. The setting was perfect, not too light and not too dark.

Hyatt and I decided to split up again. I continued to walk around the pool area and watch the festivities. Looking at all the beautiful women was the best part of the evening. The women spoke English with a definite accent, and they were considerably more reserved than the women of the Dominican Republic or Brazil. Probably a result of the cultural effects of British rule, the people of Trinidad were a lot more aloof. I could see it and feel it, and even though we shared the same language, it didn't really make a difference. I would look and they would look. But a conversation did not commence, and I had to keep on walking. Still, I looked for the woman who might be special, but I hadn't felt anything that made my heart jump. "She" may have been at the party, but I hadn't seen her...

About three hours later, I was ready to leave. Hyatt was ready to leave too. We went out to the front of the parking lot to hail a taxi. Several women were out in the parking lot also, laughing and talking and probably waiting for transportation. Some seemed to be just hanging out. They were fine. So many beautiful, available women, and no one moved me the way Therezinha had moved me—at first sight. As we waited for a taxi, we smiled at the women and began to talk about the party. Finally, an available taxi pulled up, and we went back to the hotel. I said good night to Hyatt and went to my room.

Lying in bed, I began to review the evening. Carnival was an amazing and exciting experience, I realized, no matter what country celebrates—the colors, the costumes, the music, the romance, the free and happy behavior of everyone celebrating together.

I thought, 'Everybody should go to Carnival at least once in their life!'

I had had a really good time and was ready for some sleep. In a few hours the sun would be coming up, and I was tired.

The next morning came fast. A Carnival parade was scheduled for mid-morning, and we planned to watch the parade after breakfast. We ate a big meal, talked about the night before and how the trip was going so far. In general, things were okay; this vacation was definitely different, and we both decided that the women were pretty but not very friendly. After breakfast, we left the hotel and walked down to the main street where the Carnival parade would pass. Hyatt and I took a short-cut through a field and arrived just in time. The parade was about to begin.

Hundreds of men, women and children lined both sides of the main street. Everyone stared down the street in anticipation. After awhile, band music could be heard coming around the corner. Huge, elaborate floats of all shapes and colors followed, and throngs of costumed participants walked alongside and behind the floats. Then dancing began on the sidewalks and in the streets. The streets were filled with music and laughter and noise. The celebration went on for a long time. Finally, it was over and everybody started to leave. A street party that evening would keep the excitement and Carnival energy going.

We walked back to the hotel. We decided to have lunch and then return to the hotel to rest. We were scheduled to leave the next morning for Caracas, Venezuela. Hyatt and I wanted to start the evening a little early, this time around 8:00PM. I listened to some music and rested in my room. It was about 6:00PM when I woke up. I got dressed and went to Hyatt's room.

I said, "Meet ya in the hotel restaurant in fifteen minutes."

In the restaurant, I noticed the couple from the Grand Cayman Islands we had met the other night. I said hello and asked them what their plans were for the evening.

The husband replied, "We're going to the street party!"

I told them that Hyatt and I were planning the same thing. They suggested that we all go together.

"Sounds fine," I said, "I'll tell Hyatt."

When Hyatt arrived, he said that more company was fine with him. Then we ordered a light dinner. After dinner, we left and walked outside to wait for a taxi. The taxi dropped us off downtown, and the four of us started to walk around.

We saw parties everywhere! Trucks carrying steel drum bands drove by, stopping here and there. When a truck stopped, the musicians standing at the back of the truck began to play. They sounded great!! The musicians played old oil barrels and made music. On both sides of the street, people sang and danced. How those old oil drums could make such a fantastic sound amazed me.

The four of us continued to walk down the street. The center of the street party was a few blocks ahead. As we inched down the street, the crowds widened even more. We could hardly move; our shoulders touched as we tried to reach the place where musicians were going to play. Once close enough, we stopped and waited for the music to start. At the same time, the trucks filled with musicians would pass in the street, and they excited the standing crowds.

Everyone started to dance. In time, the trucks had to nudge the people dancing in the street to the sides in order to move ahead. No one stopped dancing! The celebration had gone on for nearly three hours, and still nobody was leaving.

I yelled to Hyatt, "This is some street party!"

Both Hyatt and I knew that we had scheduled an early flight. We all decided to go. It was early morning. As we walked, we looked for a taxi. Once back at the hotel, we said good night to everyone. Once in my room, I washed my face and brushed my teeth and fell out on the bed. The next thing I knew, it was morning.

Our flight was at 6:30AM. The taxi arrived at 5:30AM, and we were ready to leave for the airport. We ran into heavy traffic on our way to the airport. We had missed our flight to Venezuela. A flight to Caracas on another airline was about to depart, and the ticket agent said that his airline would accept our tickets. We were grateful! Hyatt was ahead of me as we as we walked to the gate. Before we entered the gate area, Hyatt placed his two bags on the moving belt to his right, and then he went through the walkway. Immediately after Hyatt passed through, I did the same. The next thing I knew, a Customs officer presented himself and said that he wanted to talk to me.

I followed him to the Customs Office. Once in the office, I was asked why I was leaving Trinidad before Carnival was over. I told them that I had set my schedule that way so that I could visit another country on my vacation. They didn't seem to believe me. They called to the plane and told the pilot to wait. Then they searched my suitcase, my travel bag, and they also searched me after taking me to a little back room. I was very upset with them. They knew I was an American, and so "assumed" that I was transporting drugs. I explained to them that I was a business man and that I worked hard at what I do. Eventually, they let me go. They couldn't hold me any longer. I kept saying to them, "I don't do drugs, I don't sell drugs, and I don't transport drugs."

The plane had not left. When I reached Hyatt, he asked me what had happened. I told him and he couldn't believe it.

Still very upset, I said, "Man, it's a bad situation to be accused of something in another country and have to convince the authorities to let you go!"

My upset continued. I didn't like what I had just experienced one bit! It had started to spoil my vacation. I knew that there were drugs being shipped illegally all around the world. What on earth could I do about that? It made me realize how individuals can be subjected to a frightening detainment when they were completely innocent—and it is all the worse in a foreign setting.

I started to calm down. Before long, the captain said that we would be landing in about thirty minutes. The flight from Trinidad to Caracas, a city in the northernmost part of South America, is only about one hour. We landed in Caracas. It was early, about 10:00AM. We got off the airplane and went to get a taxi. Several taxis were parked in cue in front of the airport. Our driver took us downtown to a hotel. On the way, we saw many small houses on the hillsides. The houses stood out against the red clay dirt. Once downtown, Hyatt and I decided on a hotel and checked in. The hotel was located on the waterfront, and it had an outside cafe. We could sit down and have a meal as we looked out at the Caribbean Sea! The rooms were small, but they were manageable. We unpacked and went to the hotel's cafe for some lunch. We sat outside and looked across the Caribbean.

After lunch, we walked down by the waterfront side of the city. About half a mile into our walk, we stopped at a park. It was summer time in Venezuela, and many children were playing in the park. There were huge, flat rocks near and in the water, and people were sitting and sun-bathing on top of the rocks. We walked over to the rocks, and there we could view the entire expanse of the park. The Venezuelan women we saw were quite beautiful. The women had light-colored skin and long black hair. I also noticed that most of them had hairy legs and arms and were big-breasted. After about an hour of walking, I told Hyatt that I was going back to the hotel.

He said, "Okay, I'll see you in a little while."

About an hour later, Hyatt came back and told me that an evening event was planned at the park that night. He had overheard someone talking about it. After awhile, I got up and called Hyatt's room. He said he was ready to go, and we decided to have dinner at the hotel's cafe. There wasn't another restaurant within walking distance of our hotel. The hotel, we found out, is located on the outskirts of town, where not much was going on. We had wished that we had picked a hotel in a better location.

After dinner, we walked to the park. As we approached, we heard music and saw people dancing. We only saw couples. There didn't seem to be any single women there. Hyatt and I split up and walked around the park. Nothing else was going on. We decided to leave. It wasn't what we had expected to see, but we had to check it out. That's what we were there to do...

We walked back to the hotel. About an hour later, Hyatt came to my room and said that he was thinking of leaving Caracas a day early. He wanted to stop back in the Dominican Republic on the way back to the States. He asked me if I wanted to go with him. I didn't mind, and told him, "No problem."

The next morning, I knocked on Hyatt's door, and we left to get some breakfast. Then we walked to the park to look at the sites and relax. Caracas is a beautiful place. But for single guys on vacation, there's not much to do. On the walk back to the hotel, we decided that we'd get a taxi that evening and ride around so we could see some other sights. After all, this was our last night in town.

Back at the hotel, I decided to call my friend, Claudio in Brazil. It took a few minutes to get through to Brazil on the hotel phone. Then Claudio answered. He asked me why the operator spoke in Spanish. I told him that I was calling from Caracas, Venezuela. He asked what was I doing there. I told him that I was on vacation.

"Good for you!" he said.

Claudio and I talked for about five minutes. Everything was okay with him and Selma. I said hello to her also. I enjoyed talking with both of them. Claudio told me that Therezinha had moved into her sister's house and that Therezinha was doing okay. I asked Claudio to tell her hello from me. He said that he would. The call cheered me up. It is a good feeling to talk to friends who live in another country.

The rest of the day went by very fast. I decided to pack my clothes for tomorrow's trip back. We were going to leave early. I didn't have much to pack and finished quickly.

The evening arrived, and we went to the cafe restaurant for dinner. After dinner, we got a taxi and told our driver to drive us to the discos, especially the discos where there were women. He told us that it was a holiday and very few places were open.

We looked at each other, both of us with the same thought, 'No wonder there was nothing going on!'

Well, we rode around for a little while, and nothing was open. We returned to the hotel and sat outside and talked. The conversation focused on traveling. We realized that we had come here at the wrong time. But Venezuela is still a very nice country, and Caracas is a beautiful city. And the women are beautiful. Unfortunately, we just didn't have the opportunity to meet any single women. The conversation moved on to international carnivals. I told Hyatt that the Carnival in Trinidad couldn't match the Carnival in Rio de Janeiro. I added that Brazil had the best Carnivals in the world, and one day he should to go to Brazil during Carnival. Then he would know what I was talking about.

We went back into the hotel. We had to leave early for the airport. I asked the hotel clerk to call a taxi for us in the morning; the taxi needed to be at the hotel by 5:30AM. We wanted to get to the airport on time. I didn't want to miss another flight, especially since we were traveling back to the Dominican Republic.

When I was alone in my room, I thought about Trinidad and Venezuela. I had enjoyed myself in both places. These countries would remain special to me.

Chapter
Fourteen

The phone rang.

"Hullo," I groaned.

"Get up, the taxi's coming," Hyatt said.

Hyatt was at the front desk when I came down. We checked out.
The taxi arrived and we left for the airport.

At the airport we bought our tickets for the Dominican Republic,
checked in and waited to leave. This was a side-trip, so I thumbed
through my wallet to make sure that I had enough money for two
more days. The airport at Caracas had put in place some very tight
security. Everyone's bags were checked two and three times. Finally,
the plane was ready for boarding. Our flight back to the Dominican
Republic would take about two hours.

Before long, we had landed in Santo Domingo, the capital. We got off the plane and rented a car. We thought about a drive to Puerto Plata, the northeast region of the country, but time was of the essence. We had only planned to be in the Dominican Republic for two days; so, we decided to stay in the city.

It was still February and the weather was perfect. We drove around and found a different hotel this time. The hotel was very nice, and now Hyatt and I were in a good location too. The hotel was more central to the downtown area of the *malacon*, which was fine with me. We checked in and came directly out; we wanted to drive to town to get something to eat.

We drove down to the walking street and found a little restaurant and had lunch and talked awhile. We then decided to drive down by the *malacon* and see what was going on there. No matter what the time of day, lots of activity is bound to be happening, and there is always something to do or see. We cruised around for awhile. We even drove over to the University to check it out. The University area is a dynamic part of the city, and rallies or some other kinds of demonstrations are usually taking place. The campus bustled with young men and women walking to and from the buildings all day long. And the women were great to look at. More than that, it was good to see so many young people trying to educate themselves. After all, education is the best way for individuals to better themselves—knowledge is power, the kind of power that can never be taken away.

After leaving the University campus, Hyatt and I continued to cruise all around the island. We knew the city, Santo Domingo, very well now that we had driven through most of it. A few hours later, we decided to go back to the hotel and get ready for the evening. We would probably do some more cruising that night.

Once back in the room, I sat down and began to think. I started to wind down a little and had started to get my mind back to my business in San Francisco. I felt like I had been in a time machine for the last week or so. Even though I had enjoyed myself, international travel tends to take its toll, especially when staying on the go as Hyatt and I had been. Sometimes travelers don't realize that the body is constantly going through time zones and is trying to adjust. Since we were moving from country to country, by the end of a week, my body was tired, and it started to tell me that it was time to slow down. Personally, I like to sleep late and rest, but the only time that I can do this is when I am on vacation. So far on this vacation, I hadn't had the time to rest. I decided that I would take it easy for the next couple of days…even though I still hadn't found that special woman I had been looking for. I was as determined as ever to find her. I knew it would only be a matter of time before it happened. One thing for sure, I didn't want to rush into anything. I planned to spend the rest of my life with her, so she had to be the right one.

A knock at the door interrupted my thoughts.

"Come in," I said. Hyatt stood there, clapping his hands.

"Hey, Man, let's go and get something to eat," he said.

"Okay," I answered.

We went downstairs to the hotel restaurant and ordered dinner. Both of us ordered seafood. The seafood was fresh and delicious and we both enjoyed it. After dinner, we went back to our rooms to get dressed and leave for the evening. We had made no definite plans; we were just going to cruise around the town and stop wherever things looked interesting. We left about an hour later.

We drove around for about twenty minutes and then we went down along the *malacon*, where we saw several nice hotels, and the bars in the hotels usually had a Merengue band. We parked the car and went into one hotel noted for its gambling tables and the high-rollers who hung out there. The hotel was spectacular! The lobby was huge and decorated with blue and white walls and carved wooden furniture. Marble-like columns stretched to the ceiling. It was full of people. A money exchange is also located in the lobby, and we both exchanged some cash and walked around the hotel. A band was playing, and we decided to sit down and listen to some music. The band wasn't that good. We left and went to another hotel where we heard disco music playing. We had been in that hotel before, and we liked it, so we went in to have a drink and check it out. There wasn't much going on in the hotel. Well, it was a week night, so things were slow. I listened to the music and sipped a coke. I liked Merengue music. Merengue music is the soul of the Caribbean. After listening to several songs and after having looked around the club, we decided to leave and go back to the hotel for the night.

Our hotel had a disco on the top floor. We took the elevator to the top floor and got out. The disco's dance floor was fairly large, and the walls were mirrored. There was also a great view of the city. We could look out and see a wide span of Santo Domingo below us. It was absolutely beautiful, especially at night with twinkling lights from one edge of view to the other. We walked around the room and looked. The people there were mostly couples, so we didn't stay long. I told Hyatt that I was about ready to turn in. We left and went to our rooms. I turned on the TV. The hotel provided cable in the rooms, which was great. I found some American TV stations and tuned in as I got ready for bed. Tomorrow was the last day of my vacation, and then it was back home to work.

The next morning, as the sun shone brightly through the window of my room, I woke up feeling pretty good. I really liked the hotel, especially after the last one. And it was reasonably-priced! Just as I got out of the shower, Hyatt called to see if I was ready for breakfast.

"Just about," I said. "It's our last day here. After we eat, let's go to the beach."

We left the hotel and drove to the beach. It was about forty minutes away. The beach was crowded, and a small four-piece band, positioned on a wooden bandstand, played music, while the beach-goers listened and danced in the glistening sand. We walked around and became part of the crowd. There were some nice-looking women standing around, and they looked great in their swimsuits. Everyone seemed to be having fun as they enjoyed the Caribbean sunshine.

Hyatt and I split up. I sat near the bandstand and listened to the music. When Hyatt came back, we both decided to walk along the beach near the warm, blue water. Santo Domingo borders the Caribbean Sea, but the northeastern portion borders the Atlantic Ocean. I walked down the beach with Hyatt and enjoyed the sights—everyone seemed to be having fun, and children ran in and out of the water as their parents watched. It was a hot day, and I stopped to relax in the shade for awhile and just look out at the incredibly blue Caribbean Sea. Some young guys were out on the waves, racing around on jet skis, and falling down in the water again and again. I laughed at their antics, but it sure looked like fun! I began to walk back down the beach toward Hyatt. About halfway down, I noticed Hyatt out in the water swimming with the locals.

I yelled out to him, "Hey Hyatt, don't drown!" Both of us laughed, and he waved me along.

I started to walk back to the bandstand. The music played as loudly as ever. I glanced at the speakers next to the musicians. There were unbelievably large, and now I knew why the music could be heard all the way down the beach.

About an hour later, Hyatt came over. He was ready to go. He had gotten some water in his ear and had the start of an earache.

"Okay, let's go."

We drove back to the hotel. Hyatt went to his room, and I decided to change quickly and go back out. I wanted to be outside. I went down the beach front and sat at a cafe to watch the women go by.

It was close to 6:00PM, and most of the stores were about to close. The ladies would be leaving and walking by the cafe. I would try to talk to some of the pretty ones, as best I could, considering I didn't speak Espanol... And they would try to talk to me. Most of the time, we didn't understand one another, but believe it or not, that was half the fun! The Dominican women always smiled and were very warm and friendly. I considered girl-watching one of my favorite hobbies here in the Dominican Republic—flirting with the ladies for the fun of it. But at the same time, my heart searched for that "special" woman.

After I finished my second drink, I walked back to the hotel. Hyatt still had problems with his ear. I asked if he wanted to go out for dinner. We left a few minutes later for the *malacon*.

We stopped at a restaurant that served traditional Dominican food. It was packed from wall to wall. We finally found two free seats and ordered our food. We saw people marching up and down the streets, carrying political signs and repeating the same phrases. National elections were coming up, we had heard.

After dinner, we drove around and stopped at a couple of clubs. We didn't stay very long. After about two hours of driving around, I was ready to get back to the hotel and pack for the airport.

I was ready to go back home. The past days had been great. I was glad that Hyatt and I had stopped back in the Dominican Republic on our way back to the States. My mind felt settled, and I was ready to get back to work. I felt recharged by the trip. There were a lot of things to do between now and June, when school would be out for the summer, but I was more than ready for the task.

In the morning, Hyatt knocked at my door, and I told him I would meet him in the lobby in five minutes. We checked out of the hotel and left for the airport. It was about 6:00AM. We dropped off the rental car, then checked ourselves in, and we boarded the plane.

Once back in Miami, Hyatt and I said our goodbyes. We planned to go somewhere in the summer, but we hadn't decided on a final itinerary.

I landed in San Francisco on a Friday and had the weekend to unwind before work on Monday. This was very important to me.

Monday came before I knew it. I scheduled myself as a driver every day of the week for the rest of the school year as well as ran the business. Men and women who own their own business always work very hard in order to stay in business, especially if theirs is a small one.

The days and then the months went by fast. It was now April, and school would be out for Easter. I called Hyatt to see how he was doing. Everything was okay with him. We talked for about a half an hour, but didn't settle on a firm plan for the summer. We would talk again.

It was now springtime in California, and the weather had started to get nice again. The winter had brought a lot of rain, and the terrible weather made my job more difficult. Driving a large bus in bad weather is pretty nerve-wracking. Before long, it was time for Easter vacation in the schools. I went to visit one of my aunts. She mentioned that she, two of my other aunts and my grandfather and cousin planned a summer cruise in the Caribbean. She suggested that I come with them. They were scheduled on the cruise ship in early August.

I thought to myself, 'This could be a nice change for me!'

To tell the truth, I was a little tired of flying from country to country and being constantly on the run on every single vacation I took. This definitely would be different, lounging on a luxury cruise ship… My aunt mentioned that the ship had "everything" on it— passengers could eat all the food they wanted and have fun doing whatever activities they wanted. She told me to think about joining them and to let her know in about a week. I said I would.

As the week progressed, I began to think more seriously about the cruise and decided to go. It would be a brand new experience for me, and I could spend some time with my family. I called my aunt and told her to book me for the cruise. She was happy that I would be joining them. My grandfather and I would share a room.

Once I decided to go on the cruise, the weeks went quickly. Summer was fast approaching. The business began to get calls for summer field trips, and my summer schedule filled up. The business had been established for some years now, and I started to reap the benefits of a good reputation. I was grateful to have a lot of work at this time.

After a busy two months, I looked forward to this new "adventure" and was hoping for the best. One way or another, I would enjoy myself. That was my nature.

Chapter
Fifteen

May arrived, and I looked at the busiest summer schedule I had ever had! I started to set up my drivers' schedule to match the trips. Business was humming. I kept myself busy with my own driving schedule and at the same time tried to stay on top of the management of the business. Before long, the middle of June had arrived, school was out and summer time was here.

Therezinha sent me a letter. It was a card written in Portuguese. I called my friend, Aurea. Aurea is Brazilian and works at a restaurant I go to occasionally for dinner. She had offered to help me with the translation of any letter I received from Therezinha if she wrote to me in Portuguese. We had become good friends and she understood what had transpired between Therezinha and me. Aurea told me that she could translate the letter the next day and we set a time to meet.

The next day I drove to the restaurant, and Aurea read the card. It was a Valentine's Day card. In Brazil, Valentine's Day is celebrated in June. Therezinha wrote that she was okay and wished me the best.

She hoped that I would find happiness and that I deserved to be happy. I thanked my friend Aurea for translating for me.

It was great to hear that Therezinha was doing alright. The correspondence reminded me that we had both gotten on with our lives and had to keep looking for that "special" person who would make us feel whole. Truthfully, I was surprised that she hadn't gotten involved with anyone else by now. After all, Therezinha was beautiful and she could have any man she wanted. I figured that, like me, she was taking her time and wanted to make the right choice.

The month of August arrived, it was time to go on my cruise. The family and I flew to Miami, and we stayed overnight. We would board the ship the next day. I was now ready to sail on the Caribbean Sea—I had flown over it enough times already!

Early the next morning we left the hotel for the ship. When we arrived at the dock, we saw a block-long, shiny white ocean liner and a stream of people waiting to board. It was huge! Once I stepped on board, I couldn't believe its size—a person could forget he was on a ship. It had everything.

I thought to myself, 'Hey, this might be alright.'

It took about six hours before everyone boarded the ship. We were then off to sea. A lot of women were on the ship, and many of them were by themselves. Once out at sea, I left my room to get something to eat. A long banquet table of food was laid out magnificently for the passengers. I don't think I ever saw that much food at any one time.

Later that evening, after dinner, a party was scheduled in one of the ship's lounges. Lovely women in costumes sang and passengers danced to the music. After the show, a DJ played songs, and all the while, the ship rocked from the waves. I checked out the scene. The lounge was packed, and there were all kinds of unescorted women to choose from, if I wanted to start a conversation. There were more women than men by far, and the women were checking out the men. I stood in the crowd, looking toward the dance floor when I heard someone say, "Would you like to dance?"

The request came from a nice-looking woman and we danced. The dance floor was crowded. Everyone was doing their thing.

After we finished the dance, I walked around awhile checking out the lounge and enjoying the music. Then I headed back to my room for the night. It had been a long day. I was wondering if I would be able to sleep well on the ship. But we were cruising along, and the sea was calm, for the most part.

The next morning my grandfather and I walked to the breakfast floor. The food was presented banquet-style once again. And once again, the food was delicious. I had heard that the food on cruise ships was very good, and I can tell you that it is true.

After breakfast, I ended up by the pool. Oh boy! There were some women out there in bikinis, and they were a sight to see. The sun was hot as it beat down on the ship's deck. A passenger could do almost anything on the ship that he could do on land. The ship had absolutely everything—it was really a small city!

I decided on going to the movies to just relax in the theater. I was so comfortable that I almost fell asleep! After the movie, I took the elevator up to the food deck. As I walked along the deck, I noticed a group of people looking over the side of the ship.

'I hope we're not sinking!' I thought to myself.

My mind immediately went to an image of the Titanic and what had happened to it, even though I knew there were no icebergs in the Caribbean Sea...

I walked over to the others, and when I looked over the side, I saw nine Cubans in a raft that looked like a big inner tube. It was a pathetic sight to see. I looked down at their faces, and as they looked up at the huge, glistening ship, I saw despair in their eyes. Reality hit me straight in the face. I had heard that Cubans were always trying to leave their country, but I paid no attention—it had nothing to do with my life. Even though I had once seen a news item on television where the Coast Guard picked up refugees in the ocean, it was just a picture to me. But when I actually saw this event with my own two eyes, it really affected me. It looked as if their make-shift raft was about to sink at any moment. I noticed some water in the raft, and all that could be seen in any direction was clear, blue, Caribbean Sea. There was no land in sight—anywhere. Whew!! When you see people like that, willing to risk their lives to leave their country, it makes you wonder about a lot of things.

The captain came on the speaker system and made an announcement that we were going to stop the ship and pick up the refugees. I'm sure most of the passengers didn't know what was happening.

The ship began to move after about thirty minutes, and we continued our cruise. The captain told the passengers that the refugees had been out to sea for about three days with no food or water, and sharks had begun to follow their raft. He stated that the Coast Guard would pick them up when we stopped at our next port-of-call. I thought more about the refugees. I couldn't imagine myself in a situation like theirs.

But a person never knows what could happen in this life, and I prayed that I never have to experience such a devastating circumstance as theirs. If the captain had not boarded the refugees, they probably would have been shark meat by nightfall, and I'm sure that the captain didn't want that on his conscience. He was their last hope for survival.

After I was served lunch, I noticed an empty table and sat down to eat. A young lady came up and asked if anyone was sitting at the table.

"No, be my guest," I answered.

She sat down and we began to talk. She was from California, like me, and she worked with troubled kids as a counselor. She was very smart. I told her that it was my first cruise, and she said that she had cruised before. We talked about life in general, the ordinary lunchtime conversation. She was nice but not my type. She, like the other women on the ship, were from all parts of the United States. They were very sophisticated, career-oriented, and most of them seemed very independent. And, of course, they were very pretty. They seemed to be searching for a good man for themselves. It was the same for a man, trying to find a good woman, that "special" one.

As the week went on, I met a lot of nice women on the ship. Usually, I invited them for a drink and started a conversation. I was curious about their thoughts on different subjects and situations in life. The conversations were just great. I found it very interesting to hear how women viewed life. I certainly learned some things.

There was no time to be bored on the cruise. All kinds of activities were scheduled throughout the day, and I and the other passengers enjoyed nightly shows and other kinds of entertainment. A special show was presented every night. Each evening, my family and I had dinner together. We dressed formally for dinner, and it was kind of nice to do that. We talked about the different things we had been involved in during the day. The table servers were from Brazil, and when I could, I'd try to speak with them in Portuguese. They were nice guys, and they worked hard. Theirs wasn't an easy job—they always had to be moving. One particular night, my family and I went to the show in the main lounge. The sea had gotten rough, and the ship was rocking back and forth. For the first time I felt a little seasick. Even the entertainer was rocking back and forth on the stage.

After the show, I walked to the deck where I knew there would be dancing. I went to check out the people and the music. Let me be clear about something—there were a lot of beautiful, single, available women on the ship, but among the women on the cruise, I did not find a connection.

It was the last few days of the cruise, and I had come to know my surroundings pretty well. I resigned myself to the fact that a ship-board romance for me was not going to happen. And the ship was still rocking, and again I didn't feel that well. I left for my cabin. I decided that once we were back in Miami, I would fly to Puerto Plata for a few days instead of spending the entire week with my uncle in Fort Lauderdale.

In the morning, the sea had calmed down. I got up and went to breakfast, walked around the pool side, my favorite place on the ship, and even played a little basketball for exercise. It felt good to play. It also felt good to relax. Until this time, I hadn't had a vacation where I didn't have to worry about a thing. The ship's crew took care of everything for you. I was glad that I went on the cruise ship; it was a very good experience.

The last day went fast. We were to debark in the morning, once the ship returned to Miami. And I was ready to go by that time. One week was enough for me.

At dinner that evening, I said goodbye to my family. I wouldn't see them tomorrow, because everyone would be going in different directions. Upon debarking, all passengers must pass through Immigration. And once through Immigration, there is a wait for luggage to arrive. My aunt told me that it was a long process. After dinner, I went to my cabin to get some sleep.

In the morning, people were standing in line to go through Immigration. My aunt was right; it was difficult getting off the ship. All of the lower decks were crowded and everyone wanted to be the first off the ship. Finally, my feet were on land. I got my luggage and boarded a bus for Miami International. At the airport, I called my Uncle Willie and asked him to pick me up. Then I purchased my flight ticket to Puerto Plata. On the drive to my uncle's house, I told him of my change in plans.

All of my family in Forth Lauderdale were fine, which was good news. Later that day, I drove to my grandmother's house, and I stayed the night. My grandmother was happy to see me and enjoyed my company as much as I enjoyed hers. I told her that I would be leaving soon for the Caribbean.

She said, "I figured that. You don't stay anywhere too long." I laughed. She was funny, and she was also right.

Over the next couple of days, I visited with my family and enjoyed the good weather. It was very hot, and I tried to stay in the shade whenever I could. The days went by fast, and before I knew it, I would be leaving the next day. That night I asked my Aunt Carmen about Puerto Plata, and she and I sat at the dining room table and talked. By the time I pushed away from the table, I knew that I was going to a beautiful place in the morning and was going to enjoy myself a lot.

My Uncle Willie came to take me to the Miami airport. About thirty minutes later, I was thanking my uncle Willie and walking into the airport. I checked in and headed for the gate to board the plane. In about two hours or so, we left.

The flight arrived right on time. I got off the plane and went to Customs. No problem there. I walked out of the terminal to a car-rental place, rented a car and got directions to a hotel on the main street, not too far from downtown proper. I noticed a resort area not far from the hotel. I wasn't too tired at that time and decided to drop my bags in my room, go back out and drive to the resort area. The area I noticed is Playa Dorada. It is very beautiful. Well-kept hotels lined both sides of the street, and around the hotels were beaches, golf courses, cottages and casinos. The resort area looked like a picture postcard.

I went into one of the hotels, and hotel staff were serving lunch. I asked if I could buy lunch. A waiter dressed in a white tuxedo said, "Certainly," and sold me a ticket. I walked to the buffet table, and the food looked delicious. I noticed a lot of Europeans and Canadians in the dining room enjoying their meal. The food was excellent. After lunch, I walked around the hotel. It had a huge swimming pool, tennis courts, a horse stable for riding, a disco, a bar—everything anyone could want when on vacation. It was incredible! After walking around for awhile, I decided I would return to that hotel for dinner for sure.

Then I drove down a ways to Puerto Plata's *malacon*. It was much smaller than Santo Domingo's *malacon*, but I expected that the atmosphere would be the same, especially at night. Puerto Plata's *malacon* had lots of tourist spots: cafes, bars, and clubs, many with outside tables to take advantage of the tropical warmth and sunshine. I saw some beautiful women walking around the area. I planned to check out the discos after dinner; I wanted to see what was happening in Puerto Plata.

Nightfall had arrived. I drove back to Playa Dorada to get something to eat. After dinner, I walked around the corner to another hotel where I had earlier noticed a disco. A beauty contest was in progress. The women were lined up on the dance floor. They looked very beautiful. I watched the contest and, of course, picked my own winner. But it wasn't easy—the competition was great. The contest concluded, I was sure, when I heard all the men in the place cheering. The best-looking woman had won—I was right!

After the contest, people began to dance. The dance floor immediately filled up. I glanced across the crowd to see if I could find someone I liked. The language barrier could be an obstacle, but only if you let it. I'm sure a lot of men wouldn't want to talk to a woman who didn't speak the same language they did. For me, it was nothing more than a small challenge. Many of the tourists were women, and, to tell the truth, I wasn't very interested in them, only the Dominican women. The music was good. I enjoyed myself, even though I saw no one who could prompt me to great interest. It got late, and I left and drove back to my hotel. I would start all over again tomorrow, checking out this new paradise.

I had noticed that the women who worked at the hotels and casinos were beautiful and friendly. I saw them walking back and forth.

They spoke good English too. It was likely part of the job requirement, since they would be interacting with tourists all of the time. Spending my time in the hotels could be beneficial to my search...

My hotel served three meals a day, but to me breakfast was the best. I left to ride around more and ended up by the *malacon* and parked. I sat down at a sidewalk cafe to enjoy the sights and scenery. Puerto Plata is much smaller than Santo Domingo. To me, it felt more beautiful and peaceful than Santo Domingo. I didn't see as many women there, but the women I did see were as beautiful as anywhere.

After my rest stop, I drove around the downtown area. It was crowded with people walking around and shopping and beginning their weekend holiday. The downtown area didn't have a walking street, as in Santo Domingo. I drove around, learning my way here and there. It was easy for me, since I drove for a living. However, the Dominicans drive haphazardly, compared to American drivers; so I had to be very alert. I found that I was getting used to Puerto Plata. It didn't take me long to adjust. Even though I was by myself, I liked it. It gave me a chance to reflect on my life up to this point. I had to keep focused on the things I wanted in life and to keep striving for them.

I went back to the resort area, and after lunch, I took a long walk. I went down to the beach front, then headed back to the hotel. I wanted to rest, and then get ready for the evening.

Puerto Plata weather is hot, and three showers a day are needed in order to stay fresh. I didn't mind at all.

I stayed at the hotel until early evening. It was time to go have dinner. I planned to go to a little restaurant next to the hotel that served barbecued chicken. The owner of the restaurant spoke English, and we talked while I ate his delicious chicken. It was good as any barbecued chicken I could get in San Francisco. I returned to my room to get ready to go to the *malacon*. After all, it was Friday, and I was ready to meet some women.

On the drive to the *malacon*, I saw throngs of people walking in the street, talking and laughing and enjoying themselves. The crowds made me feel in a holiday mood. At the *malacon*, Merengue music played in the street and many cars were parked down by the water. Cars cruised up and down the *malacon*. I finally found a parking place and headed for a cafe, which had a disco on its top floor.

I decided to sit at a cafe table and have a drink before going up to the disco. I sipped a coke, and watched the women walking upstairs to the club. Many women were on their way to the disco, and the sights were lovely! I was in no hurry to go in—I just wanted to watch the scene. I stayed at the cafe for a long time, watching everybody pass back and forth. Quite a few other men hung around the cafe, also watching the traffic.

I finally decided to check out the disco. I paid the required pesos and went in. Lucky for us tourists, the American dollar goes a long way in the Dominican Republic. Once inside, I saw that the club was fairly new and much larger than I expected. The music played and the women stood around, waiting to dance. I walked around the floor, as usual, looking at everyone. It was a very nice club and had a good atmosphere. Most of the tables were already occupied by couples, so I stood by the bar and watched the action on the dance floor and around it. I had a good spot; I could easily see the people coming and going. Women walked by the bar. I stared at them and they stared back. It was funny.

After standing at the bar for awhile, I realized that there weren't many single women in the club as I had thought, and I didn't want to dance just to dance. I was on a mission, looking for that "special" woman with whom I could start a serious relationship. She wasn't there.

I left the disco for the hotel to get ready for bed. I would only have tomorrow, Saturday, and then I would have to leave.

I didn't get up for breakfast. It felt good to stay in my cozy bed. I finally decided to get up and showered and dressed. I drove to Playa Dorada for lunch. I sat down at an outside cafe and ordered a light lunch. After lunch, I thought I might drive around the island and find something to do on my last day.

As I drove out of the resort area, I saw a woman walking down the left side of the street. She had long, black silky hair that moved gently back and forth as she walked. As I passed by, I looked at her and saw how very pretty she was. I decided to stop the car about twenty feet in front of her. I wanted to take a picture of her as she walked by the car. A motorcycle was right behind me, and the driver stopped. The woman began to cross the street. I thought that she might be getting a ride from the motorcycle driver, and I wouldn't be able to take her picture.

I had come to know how "brotherly" and "sisterly" island people were, and it didn't supprise me that one stranger would ask another stranger for a ride, if it were necessary.

I was just about to drive off when I noticed that she waved the motorcycle off. Then she walked up to the passenger side of my car and she got in.

"What is your name?" I asked her.

"My name is Ana Julia," she replied.

"Nice to meet you. My name is Kevin. Where are you going?"

"To the University…to school…and I'm late," she said.

She reminded me of Therezinha. Her facial features were similar to Therezinha's, and her smile too. Ana Julia told me that she worked in one of the luxury resorts, and that was probably why her English was so good. And that was great for me! She asked me to take her to her house for a minute to get a school book.

"No problem," I said.

She showed me the way to her house, went in and came right out. Then we went to the University. On the way there, I asked her if she was married. She said that she wasn't. Any children? "No," she answered. I told her that I wasn't married either and that I was divorced and had no children.

Once we got to the University, Ana Julia thanked me. She said that she would have been late for class if I hadn't helped her. We exchanged phone numbers, and I told her that I was leaving for California tomorrow. She then left hurriedly for her class.

I was excited to met her. She seemed very nice, and I enjoyed talking to her. She had definitely made an impression on me. One thing bothered me, though. Ana Julia reminded me of Therezinha, and I had to be careful not to compare her to Therezinha, if there was a chance for a relationship between us.

I remained conscious of this fact. At the same time, I had to pursue Ana Julia; I wanted to see what would happen between us…

I left the University and drove around the island awhile. Then I went back to the hotel to get ready for dinner. Well, it had been a pretty good day. I hadn't met anyone new in a long time whom I actually liked. I thought about it some more. I would take things nice and slow, that's my style. I was ready to start another foreign relationship with a woman. Actually, I missed the correspondence I used to have with Therezinha. Nowadays, I would get a card or letter only on special occasions. After dinner, I rode around the *malacon* for about an hour and relaxed as I looked at the crowds and the scenery. Then I decided to drive back to my hotel and turn in for the night.

In the morning, it was time for me to leave. I had gotten my trip to Puerto Plata, the northern part of the Dominican Republic, and I had really enjoyed my summer vacation. I was definitely recharged and ready to go home and back to my business.

On the way to the airport, I stopped by Ana Julia's house to say goodbye to her. She wasn't at home. The landlady said that she had gone to her parents' house. I asked the landlady if she would tell Ana Julia that I had come by. I thanked her and drove off, heading for the airport.

I had about an hour wait at the airport. Then I boarded the plane for Miami. The flight was as smooth as silk. After I boarded another plane for San Francisco, I folded my arms, snuggled into my seat and slept most of the way to the West Coast.

There were some problems at the business in my absence. Nothing major. I handled the problems immediately. In my stack of mail, I noticed a card from Therezinha. It was a card wishing me a happy birthday. She also wrote that her youngest sister, Denise, had had a baby girl, which was good news. Therezinha said she was working every day and was doing alright. I was glad that she was doing well; I wanted her to be happy too.

Later that first week, a business associate told me that he was getting married in Denmark, and he wanted me to come to his wedding. I had worked with him in the summers, providing transportation for him and his students. He was Danish and was marrying an American woman. I was delighted to be invited, and said that I would attend his wedding. He told me that he would book my hotel and make all of the necessary arrangements for me. The wedding was to be held in a month.

The days flew by. The new school year had started. My business was doing well, and the work days hummed along with a full and regular momentum. My contracts were in place, and I could depend on my drivers.

I decided to call Ana Julia before my trip to Denmark. I wanted to see how she was doing. She said that she was fine. I told her that I would be out of town for awhile. When I came back, I would plan a trip to see her in October. She seemed excited about my plan to visit Puerto Plata soon. I told her that we needed to spend some time together in order to get to know one another. She agreed. We both said goodbye and hung up the phone. I sat there and began to think about her.

Maybe Ana Julia and I could start a relationship…

Chapter
Sixteen

The time had come for me to leave for Denmark. I had looked forward to this trip, my first time in Europe and a different experience. I flew from San Francisco to Seattle, along with the bride's family. All of us changed planes and flew on to Denmark. From Seattle the flight took ten hours. A long flight!

After a bumpy landing, my friend and his fiancé picked us up, and we drove straight to the hotel. I checked in and told him that I planned to rest for awhile. He said he would call me later.

The weather in Denmark was cold, and the hotel hadn't yet turned on the heat for the winter. I complained to the hotel representative, and she said that the heat would be turned on soon. The room was small but immaculately clean—no complaints. My friend's wedding was scheduled for Saturday. It was now Tuesday. He had planned an itinerary for all of his guests. His brother was a bus driver and would pick up the wedding guests, who were at the different hotels, and take them to see the local attractions. He would also drive them to the wedding. I stayed in the hotel for most of the day. It rained non-stop, and I didn't want to walk in the rain and get sick. My friend called and said to meet him tomorrow downtown; his brother would pick me up at noon.

"Okay," I replied. "See you tomorrow."

I had brought a lot of paperwork with me on this trip. I thought about starting my work, and then I realized that I was pretty hungry. Most of the day had gone by, and I wanted to get something to eat. I left the hotel and found a little restaurant about two blocks from the hotel. After dinner, I went directly back to the hotel. I wasn't going back out in that weather.

The hotel served breakfast, and the next morning I went downstairs to the hotel's restaurant. Then I went back to my room and did some more paperwork. About two hours later, I left to meet the others who were going downtown. My friend had arranged a meeting place where his wedding guests could gather and wait for his brother and the bus. It was a five-minute walk. There I met some of the other guests. We began to talk, and soon the bus came.

A tour of the city was the plan for the afternoon. It was a cold, breezy day. We managed to get to all of the tourist spots in the local area. The scenery was quite pretty, and the end-of-summer foliage was still very lush and green. After touring for about three hours, we were going to experience a traditional Danish lunch. Traditional fare consists mainly of sausages, sandwich meats and cold sides of pickled fish and vegetables. It was good. After lunch, we boarded the bus and drove to see some old Danish castles, castles built by kings who lived during the time of the Vikings. The castles were huge! We stopped and toured inside one of the castles, slowly walking from one enormous room to another. One would actually have to see it to believe it. I was quite amazed at the size of it. We returned to the bus, and soon we were back in the city and being dropped off at our hotels. What a day it had been!

When I walked into my room, I found that the heat had not been turned on. And I was not happy about it. After resting for awhile, I left to find a place to have dinner. I noticed a tourist-like "walking" street, similar to the one in the Dominican Republic, but much longer and with many more stores. I walked down the street and looked in the shops as I passed by. I went into a kind of deli and bought something to eat and returned to the hotel. There wasn't much happening in the city. It was fairly quiet. Nobody bothered me. I wasn't worried about it, but when in a foreign country for the first time, I think it's wise to show some caution. And you have to look like you know what you are doing, even if you don't, especially if you are alone.

It had started to rain again after dinner, and I hadn't brought an umbrella with me. I didn't anticipate the cold weather and hurried back to the hotel. It was still raining the next morning. My friend's itinerary planned for everyone to meet at the park. But with the cold and rainy weather, I passed. It was the kind of icy cold weather that froze your bones.

I stayed in my room and finished my paperwork that day. I completed the work, which was good for me, and at the same time I was able to relax and not worry about anything. After working for a couple of hours, I stopped to take a break. I began to think of my friends, Claudio and Selma. I hadn't spoken to them since February. I went downstairs to the lobby phone and had the overseas operator make the call. I told Claudio that I was in Denmark, that a friend of mine was getting married, and I was here for the wedding. Then Claudio asked me if I was married yet. I told him, "Not yet, but I hope to be married some time next year if things go right." He wished me luck. I asked him how he and Selma were doing. He said that all was fine with his family. I didn't talk long because the call was so expensive. We both said goodbye and hung up.

Again, in the evening, I found a place close by, ate a quiet dinner, and returned to the hotel. It had been a long day. Hopefully, the hotel would turn on the heat the next day, which was Friday.

My friend called me the next morning and said to meet him at the meeting place at 5:00PM. The bus would come and everyone would be having dinner together. The weather was about the same—dismal, cold and wet. I left the hotel and walked around a little bit, just to get some fresh air. The hotel still hadn't turned on the heat, but I had gotten used to sleeping in my clothes by now!

I returned to the hotel around noon and stayed in until it was time to leave for dinner. The bus came, and we went out. I realized that only the male guests had been invited. We were all going to have dinner with the groom. We went to the restaurant and were escorted to the back of the dining room, where we were seated at six long tables in a private room. The waiters began to serve us, and everyone ate, drank and got very merry. The Danes drink a lot and seem to really enjoy themselves. The men ordered beer, and so did I, a non-alcoholic beer. Everyone drank and made toasts to the groom. It was great to see all of the good spirit among the group. I had a great time, and the men there were nice.

After about three hours, we decided it was time to leave. The groom left for his home—he was getting married the next day. I and a couple of other guys walked to a bar where the patrons were singing karaoke. In Denmark, karaoke is very popular, and people swarm to karaoke bars. The bar was small and packed. Women sang along to different songs, and I looked around, as usual, checking out the scene. There were some very good-looking women in the bar. But they weren't my type. Not that I didn't like the women in Denmark—I certainly did. It was just that the bar gave every indication of being a kind of "meat market." It was different for me… And, there was no possibility for dancing there. The people around me sang, drank, talked and tried their best to make a "catch" for the night. It became more crowded by the minute. Eventually, I told the other guys that I would see them tomorrow at the wedding.

Whew! I was out of that wild bar and on my way to the hotel, about a thirty-minute walk. All I had to do was to walk down the "walking" street, and my hotel was located on the other side. It was about 11:00 PM. This tourist street also had a bar or a club on every block. People were hanging out on the streets, talking and planning where to go next. I saw a crowd of women taking up the entire sidewalk as they looked for clubs. I walked down the street and back to the hotel just in time because it had started to rain again. I was glad to be inside and warming up. The wedding was the next day, and it would be a very long day.

By morning the rain had stopped. It was still cold and cloudy. The bus arrived at 12:30PM to pick us up and take us to the castle where the marriage ceremony would be held. We boarded and left. We picked up more guests on the way, and by the time we arrived at the castle, the bus was full. Dressed in our finest, we went into the castle and toward the castle's chapel.

It was beautiful inside. We went to our seats and waited for the ceremony to begin. After about thirty minutes, the ceremony began. The bride had arrived and she was beautiful. The ceremony only lasted about fifteen minutes, a very short ceremony. We all left for the reception hall, which was right across the street. The bride and groom arrived at the reception in a horse-driven buggy. Then their family members arrived. Everyone congratulated them.

The bus came an hour later and took all the guests to a restaurant for dinner and the afternoon celebration. A Danish wedding lasts the whole day. We all sat down and introduced ourselves. There were guests from all over the world, a truly international group. I talked to most of the Danish guests—very nice people, very nice to talk to and cordial to their foreign guests. All Danes speak three languages—Danish, English and Swedish. Very impressive. I enjoyed myself tremendously, having been able to talk with different people and learn about different cultures. The dinner reception went on until midnight, and then the dancing started. After more socializing, we were served another meal. When the Danes celebrate, they go all the way! At close to 2:00AM, the bus came and we left for the city.

It was late morning when our bus arrived to take us to a ferry station. We were all going to Sweden, the country across the water. Most of the guests talked about the wedding and what a wonderful time they had had. I noticed that some had gotten to know each other well. I was happy to be with such a nice group of people. Unfortunately, the weather was still cloudy and cold. The bus came, and we headed for the ferry station. We boarded the ferry and left on what I was sure were some very cold waters. The ferry ride to Sweden takes about forty minutes. We had not planned to go into the country; we would ride on the ferry to the edge of the country and come right back, a turn-around. Food and hot drinks were offered on the boat. It was now Sunday, and I would be leaving the next day. I saw the country, Sweden, from the boat. We stayed on the ferry for about ten minutes, and then we started back over the waters to Denmark. It was something to do for the day. We boarded the bus and went to the family house of the groom to say goodbye to the newly-weds and to wish them a happy honeymoon.

The bus returned and picked up the guests to take everyone back to their hotels. Once in my room, I started to pack my clothes. Hallelujah! The hotel had finally turned on the heat! I sat at the desk in my room and finished the last of my paperwork. The rest of the day I just relaxed. Later that night, I walked down to the "walking" street and had dinner at one of the restaurants. Afterward, I returned to the hotel. The day was over.

I arrived at the airport early and checked in. I browsed at a newsstand as I waited to depart Denmark. The plane was crowded. It would be a long flight back. After the flight attendants served breakfast, I fell asleep. Then later, I watched a movie and just sat there like everyone else, waiting to hear that our plane was about to land.

It had been a good trip for me.

Chapter
Seventeen

It was Monday, a school holiday, then back to work. No weekend to rest. Ana Julia had left messages for me at the office. I called her and told her the dates she could expect me next month. Everything was fine with the business. In the last years I had worked very hard to get contracts, all types of work, wherever I could find it, and now I could see an established business with a solid reputation. I could travel and hardly be missed—I liked that.

The month passed in a whirl. Already it was October, and one week later, I left for Puerto Plata. I arrived and rented a car and drove to Ana Julia's job to wait for her. She expected me. She looked as good as I remembered, and we went out for dinner at a restaurant in the *malacon*. She talked about her family, and I talked about mine, and we just talked about general things. After dinner, we rode around a little. Then I drove her back home. She had to be up early for work.

"Good night, I'll see you tomorrow."

She said, " Okay. Same time and place."

I had enjoyed dinner with Ana Julia and it felt good to be back in Puerto Plata.

I slept in and rested. Around noon, I left and drove down to the resort area for lunch. Then I walked around and checked out the sights. Of course, tourists were everywhere. The place looked full. After walking for awhile around the resorts, I decided to drive down by the *malacon* and relax by the water. It was very peaceful down there. I parked by the water. I sat on the beach and thought for what had to have been hours. I cleared my mind of everything, which was good for me to do.

It was time to leave and pick up Ana Julia from work. She came out to meet me. She had to go to school, back to the University. I told her that I would pick her up after her classes and take her home. I had a bite to eat and I rode around the island for awhile. Then I returned to the University to pick her up. It was about 9:00PM. She was tired. I could see it in her face, as I drove her home. I wanted to spend more time with her, but that wasn't going to happen. She was a very busy person, committed to keeping her goals. I respected her for that and didn't want to interfere. She reminded me more and more of Therezinha, a hard worker, committed to making her life better. The resemblance between these two women amazed me. I was ten years older than Ana Julia and could see that she was already trying to make something positive happen for herself.

Back at her house, we said good night. I told her that I would see her tomorrow. The day had gone by relatively fast.

The next day, I discovered some new places in Puerto Plata.
I enjoyed the time to myself during the day. Free to do anything I
wanted. The weather was perfect. The day slipped away quickly.

Five o'clock had come. It was now time to go and get Ana Julia.
Again, she was always happy to see me. And she liked to speak to me
in Espanol—which I was starting to pick up a little. She lived in a
little, one-bedroom apartment, and it was nice. It was very small,
but just perfect for her. We talked for awhile. Then she had to get
ready for school. Soon we left for the University. I told Ana Julia that
I wouldn't be back that night, but the next day, Friday, I wanted to
see her. A Merengue festival down at the *malacon* was planned for
Friday, and a parade was scheduled too. She knew all of this, of
course. People had talked about it during the week. I asked if she
would go with me.

She said, "I'll let you know Friday."

I stopped at a small diner in the University area and had dinner.
Then I drove around. I started to think about Ana Julia and me.
Sometimes I felt that, even though she liked me, she was running
away from me at the same time. It was like chasing after a butterfly
without a net! But the challenge was certainly intriguing. She was a
very nice, quiet woman with all the physical features I liked. Even
though she reminded me of Therezinha, I was attracted to her for
who she was.

I drove to the resort area the next day for lunch. I wanted to take
Ana Julia out to lunch this week, but she always ate at work.
I walked around, as I usually did. Playa Dorada is absolutely
beautiful. After awhile, I was tired of walking around and decided to
leave. The day dragged by. Down by the *malacon*, people were

putting up banners and places to sell drinks and a stage for the music. The town was getting ready for the Merengue festival. Excitement was in the air!

In the evening, I drove back to the *malacon* and had dinner at a restaurant and listened to some music. I was looking forward to seeing Ana Julia the next day.

I woke up well-rested. It was going to be a beautiful day. During breakfast at the resort, I overheard the tourists talk about the festival. Puerto Plata is very small—tourists can only do so much when staying there. It is not the same as visiting a city like Santo Domingo, where things are going on everywhere and all of the time.

The *malacon* was blocked off to cars because of the parade scheduled later. So, I drove around the outskirts of Puerto Plata. There were homes on the hillsides, but the roads were not paved and there were a lot of potholes. I had explored the island during my visits, and driving around at night back in the country was a little scary because there were no street lights to show you the road.

I drove to Ana Julia's house to see if she wanted to go to the festival. She wasn't there. Her landlord came out and handed me a note. Ana Julia wrote that she had to go to her parents' house and would be gone all weekend. I planned to leave the next day. I wouldn't get to see her before I left. I was disappointed that she wasn't there, but I understood.

I still wanted to go to the parade. It would be starting soon and I wanted to get a good view of it. There was a lot of traffic as I maneuvered the car to the *malacon*. Finally, I found a parking space close enough to walk, and I parked the car.

People lined up on both sides of the street. It seemed as if everybody on the island was there watching for the start of the festival—tourists, families with their children, old folk. A party atmosphere was in the air. Everybody seemed to be ready. After about an hour, the parade began. Dancers came down the street, followed by floats and brightly-colored trucks filled with musicians. Everyone was singing and dancing. The music was so loud that it could probably be heard in the next country, which is Haiti! As the parade passed by the crowds along the street, the people began to dance where they stood. Everyone seemed to get along. As I walked around looking at the women in the crowd, I realized there were some pretty women looking back. I enjoyed myself and the sights, even though I wished Ana Julia had come to the festival with me.

After the parade, people still stayed in the street talking and laughing with one another. The outside cafes were packed with people. Tourists could be seen everywhere, sitting and drinking, and looking at the people who were dancing and singing. I began to get tired as I walked around through the crowds.

Back at the hotel now, I got ready for bed. I thought about Ana Julia's note. I wished I could have gotten to know her better. That was my main purpose of the trip, but it didn't happen.

I checked out of the hotel the next morning and headed for the airport. I was back in San Francisco by Friday.

The weather had started to change in California. It was beginning to feel like winter. I dug in, and found myself working every day, working hard! The month went by fast. It was already November. I called Ana Julia and asked her if she wanted me to come back to visit her. She said "Yes." I told her that I wanted to spend more time with her than I did last time. She understood and said she would try to spend more time with me.

"Okay, then I'll be back in December when school lets out for Christmas vacation, and I'll spend the holidays in Puerto Plata."

"Okay, see you then," she replied.

I contemplated just forgetting her and moving on, but I decided to give things another chance to develop. Why not?

Thanksgiving had arrived. School would be out in three weeks for Christmas. I enjoyed Thanksgiving with my family. A couple of days later, my friend Aurea invited me to come to her party. She planned to leave for Brazil and would be there for several months at least. She wanted to have a party to say goodbye to all her friends in San Francisco. I could hear Aurea's party before I parked my car. A Brazilian band was playing, and her apartment was crowded with people dancing to Brazilian songs. Aurea had a lot of friends. I hadn't realized how many Brazilians were in San Francisco—quite a few! The music reminded me of Brazil during Carnival. I wished Aurea a safe flight home and all the best. She gave me her phone number in Brazil and told me to stay in touch with her.

The year had flown by, I realized. December had come, and school was out. I sent Therezinha a card before I left, wishing her a Merry Christmas and Happy New Year. She was still on my mind, and I thought of her often.

The flight was smooth all the way to the Dominican Republic. It was Tuesday when I arrived, and on Sunday, it would be Christmas. The weather was nice and sunny. Ana Julia seemed happy to see me. She said that her school was out for a couple of days, and she only had to work. Good—we could spend a little more time with one another.

We went to her house and talked. I told her that I wanted to start a serious relationship with her, but only if she wanted the same. I asked her to think about it and let me know soon. Then she said that she wanted to go to her mother's house. I told her that I would take her there. I asked if she wanted to change before we left. I had to go to the hotel anyway, and I would be back in thirty minutes. When I returned, I saw that a friend of hers from the University had come over, and she was talking with him. Finally he left, and she decided that she didn't want to go to her mother's. So, we went to dinner instead. She looked tired—I could look into her big, brown eyes and tell.

We went to a restaurant by the *malacon* and had dinner and talked. After dinner, we rode around for awhile, just cruising and talking. Finally, I drove her home for the night, kissed her gently on the cheek and asked if she wanted to go the movies tomorrow night. She said "Yes."

The day had been good and I was tired and ready for bed.

The resort was really crowded with Christmas holiday tourists soaking up the island sunshine. It was a beautiful morning, so I left and drove down to the *malacon*, parked and hung out. It was rather quiet for a change. I looked out at the North Atlantic Ocean and saw the US Coast Guard patrolling the water. At that particular time, democracy was being restored to Haiti.

It was time to get Ana Julia from work. She wanted to study for awhile at home before we left. The movie started later in the evening. I went to have dinner. She was waiting for me when I arrived, and we drove to the movie theater. We were right on time—the movie was just about to start. We saw a comedy about two cowboys from New Mexico who traveled to New York to find their kidnapped friend. It was pretty funny.

We both sat there, watching the movie. Ana Julia was sitting to my right. I looked over at her, and I realized that Ana Julia would be the closest I could get to finding a woman similar to Therezinha, in terms of looks, inner beauty and intelligence. We seemed to get along with each other very well.

After the movie was over, we left. It had been good to see her laugh and enjoy herself. She needed to do that. I knew that she had to go to work the next day. I took her home and said good night. She started to feel more comfortable, I thought, which was very important in any relationship. And I started to get to know her a little better, but not much. She was hard to figure. I had to keep playing it nice and slow.

The next morning I slept in since I had nothing to do. After lunch, I didn't do very much other than walk around the resort area until Ana Julia got off work. I then took her to the University. School had started up again. She told me that she would get a ride home, no problem. I didn't do much that night. I had dinner and turned in. Ana Julia had said she appreciated me picking her up and taking her to where she needed to go; otherwise she would have had to walk or catch the bus. That was the least I could do for her. The next day I called her, and she told me she had to go to her mother's house for the next two days. She would be back on Christmas night and asked if I would come by.

I said, "Okay, I'll stop by."

And then we said goodbye to one another.

Because it was Christmastime, there wasn't much going on around the island. It was pretty quiet. I thought about taking Ana Julia on a trip away from Puerto Plata, as a kind of little vacation. She once mentioned that she had never been anywhere. Maybe a change of scenery would be beneficial. And it would give us the opportunity to spend more time together, a necessary step if we were ever going to enter a serious relationship. I didn't know when she would have vacation time from her job, but I planned to ask her on Christmas.

On Christmas Day, I had to kill time until I could see Ana Julia, and the day seemed to drag by. When the evening arrived, I drove to her house and she was waiting for me, sitting on her porch with her landlord. I greeted both of them, "*Felice Navidad!*"

They said the same. We began to talk. I gave Ana Julia a Christmas card and she told me that she had one for me and that she would give it to me tomorrow. She had forgotten it at her job. I asked her when her vacation was. She said March or April. I told her that I was not coming back here to visit until she had a vacation, and perhaps then we would travel somewhere. She said she would find out when she would get some vacation time and let me know. I stayed and talked with both of them for awhile. This time we did spend a little more time together, and I enjoyed her more this time than the last time I was at her home. It was clear that Ana Julia liked me, but I didn't know how much at this point in time. I had done everything to let her know what kind of man I was, and she could take it or leave it. It was getting late, and she had to work tomorrow. I kissed her on the cheek and said goodbye to her.

I drove back to Playa Dorada, the hotel where I had breakfast earlier. The hotel had put on a Christmas show. It was funny. I stayed for a little while.

Then it started to rain. I saw two women walking quickly down the street. When they saw that I was going to my car, they asked me for a ride.

I said, "No problem."

The women worked at the Casino Hotel. One of them told me she had been married and had two kids. She was now separated from her husband. Her friend had never been married. The older woman asked me a question.

"Since I have been married and have two kids, do you think I'll find someone else to marry me?"

I looked at her and said, "You will. Know why?"

She said, "No, why?"

I said, "Because you're pretty."

She smiled and said, "Thank you."

I dropped them both off and said "Merry Christmas" and drove off to the hotel. I finished packing and went to bed.

I checked out of the hotel in the morning and went to say goodbye to Ana Julia. She came out and gave me my Christmas card and said, "Goodbye."

On the flight back home to San Francisco, I reflected on the past year and thought, 'I wonder what is going to happen next year?' I knew only time would tell.

Chapter
Eighteen

There was a Christmas card from Therezinha in the mail when I got home. She wished me a Merry Christmas and a Happy New Year. She also wrote that she had heard that I was getting married soon. She wished me happiness. I was surprised at what she had written. I thought, 'Why was she saying this?' And then I remembered my last conversation with Claudio back in September.

Six days later the new year arrived. It was now January 1995. School was back in session, and the new year was moving ahead. I sent Therezinha a birthday card, and in the card I wrote that I wasn't married, and was still a single man looking to remarry soon. And then I asked if it was too late for the two of us to start over again. If she thought it wasn't, then let me know.

Therezinha
In early December, I began to think that I had to leave my job. I needed it, but it wasn't good for me. I couldn't stand it anymore. I did everything to get fired. I wanted to start a new life. Even if Kevin didn't accept me

anymore. After he had told me all of those things in his letters, he might have changed his mind—I didn't care. I wanted to start all over again. And that's when I was laid off, December of 1994.

We always make the end of the year the beginning of a new one. I spent New Year's Eve on the beach with my friends, Ana and Denise. At midnight, I prayed to God to open my mind and wished that everything would go well in my life. I think I was heard. Kevin wrote me in January of 1995. I felt I was told something. He sent me a card for my birthday, and that was nice. He also sent me flowers, and that was even nicer. I realized then, I was ready...

About two weeks later, I received a note from the postal service to pick up a letter. The letter was from Brazil. Therezinha had sent me a registered letter. I waited until I got home and then opened it. She had responded to my question. According to her letter, she had thought I had gotten married again. She was happy that I hadn't. She wrote that she would like to start our relationship over again. This was exciting—the possibility of us getting together again. It had been a long time since we talked this way. I was willing to make it work this time and not let her get away like before.

I sent some flowers to Ana Julia and told her I wasn't coming back and wished her the best. Our relationship had never developed into anything serious. Therezinha and I had a history, and we were closer in age, more compatible and shared similar thoughts and views. If a relationship was going to endure, it had to have that kind of foundation.

February arrived, and I sent Therezinha a Valentine's Day card. In the card was a letter where I told her that I wanted to see her again and would visit in April. I wanted to spend Easter with her.

We hadn't seen each other in over two years! That was a long time ago. So much had happened to me in that time, but I knew that I would ask her to marry me again. If marrying her in Brazil would be the only way for us to be together, I would do that. It didn't matter to me, not this time around.

I had been working hard, and the days flew by. It was spring before I knew it. At long last, the weather warmed up; it had been an extremely cold winter, for San Francisco, that is. The sun shone every day now, and I looked forward to seeing Therezinha's beautiful face again.

I decided to send Therezinha a card. In the card, I asked her once again to marry me. I wanted her to know how serious I was about the relationship. By sending the card with my offer of marriage, she could think about it, and give me her answer when I arrived. Now, it was just a matter of time before we would be face to face again and she would tell me her answer.

In April, school was out for Easter vacation. It was time for me to leave for Brazil. I asked my friend Claudia to call Therezinha. I met Claudia through Aurea at the restaurant, and she promised to help me with translation in Aurea's absence. Claudia could tell Therezinha what flight I was taking and what time she could pick me up at the airport.

I flew from Los Angeles, and this time I booked a non-stop flight. It was a very long flight—a straight twelve hours. On the way down to Brazil, I thought to myself that Therezinha had come back into my life, and this time everything felt right. Even though we hadn't spent much time together—the distance between us had been a huge obstacle—I knew her through our correspondence in the same way she knew me. And as strange as it may seem, a person can actually get to know another very well through the exchange of written words. Of course, it takes longer, but by now Therezinha and I had been writing to each other for years. It had been our way of communicating with one another.

The pilot said that we would be landing shortly. Twelve hours in the air! I was ready to jump off the plane by the time we landed. I looked around and didn't see Therezinha right away. Then I saw her and her sister Celia and Celia's husband John walking toward me. Therezinha still looked great!

We left the airport quickly. John drove us to the Ipanema Inn Hotel, where I would be staying. It was good to be back in Brazil—everything looked just about the same. When we got to the hotel, I checked in and went directly to my room. John said that he would come back for me in about three hours, and after my rest he would take me to Therezinha's house. It was so good to see her again. She made me smile.

The hours passed, and I went down to the hotel lobby to wait for John. We left for Therezinha's house. She was now staying with her older sister Rose Angela and Rose Angela's husband George and their two sons. We arrived at the house about an hour later. Therezinha's mother was there. I greeted her and Therezinha's sisters. Her friend, Ana was also there to greet me.

I chatted with Therezinha's sisters as best I could on the back patio, and then Therezinha called me to come to the telephone.

"Hello?"

It was Claudio. Therezinha had called him so that we could talk. It was good to hear his voice. He was out of town on business. Claudio mentioned that if he could, he would stop over to see me before I left. Claudio knew why I had come back to Brazil. I had to have her answer, I couldn't wait any longer. I asked him to ask Therezinha for her answer. Is it "Yes" or "No?" He said that he would translate my statements. I handed Therezinha the phone.

When they finished talking, she handed the phone back to me.

"What is her answer?"

Claudio said, "Sit down, Kevin." I sat down on the bed.

Then he replied, "She said 'Yes.'"

Wow, I was so elated! We were going to be married! I couldn't believe it! I was the happiest man in the world! I then asked Claudio to be my best man. He said he would.

Therezinha was happy too. She smiled and her face glowed. I thanked Claudio for translating for us and hung up the phone.

Therezinha
I was so happy that Kevin told my mom and the rest of my family that he wanted to be engaged. I thought it was cool. It was very different. I never thought this could happen to me. In Brazilian culture, it is customary to ask the parents for the hand of their daughter.

At the end of the evening, John drove me back to the hotel. I said thank you and good-night to everyone. I kissed Therezinha good night. My head was spinning. I wanted to get married in July, which was only three months away. We had so much to do and so little time to do it!

In the morning, the phone rang. It was Therezinha. She said that her cousin Marcia wanted to make dinner for us, and we could spend Wednesday evening at Marcia's house.

Rio de Janeiro's weather was nice this time of year. The beach front was filled with *caricoas*, as usual. Nothing much had changed. Ipanema's beach looked the same as I remembered. After my walk, I went back to the hotel to get ready for dinner. Before long it was evening.

After dinner, I decided to call my friend, Aurea. She was at home and happy to hear my voice in Brazil. I told her that Therezinha and I planned to be married in July. Aurea was very happy for me. She wanted to meet Therezinha, so we planned to get together on Friday night. She said that she would also have a friend with her. I thought that meeting Aurea would be good for Therezinha. She could talk to Aurea and ask her questions about California for herself. This way Therezinha would have some idea of what to expect when she came to San Francisco.

The rest of the day passed quietly for me. I did a lot of thinking that day. I wanted to make sure that things were going to be good for her and me. I knew that her life would be changing dramatically, and my life would also be changing.

John was expected at 7:00PM. Evening arrived, and John drove me to Therezinha's house. We picked her up and then left for Marcia's house. It was good to see Marcia. Since I had visited last, Marcia and Marcos had a baby girl, and they named her Mila. Marcos told me that they were doing fine. It was good to see him again also.

We had a wonderful dinner, and the rest of the evening was spent discussing wedding plans. Marcia was happy that Therezinha and I were getting married.

Then we watched some TV and talked some more. We discussed the amount of paperwork that would need to be attended to in order to get married in Brazil. I soon realized that it was not going to be easy to get through the procedures, particularly since an American was going to marry a Brazilian. It was going to require a lot of patience and time in order to be done legally. Marcia explained the way things worked in Brazil. Very slowly. She gave me some kind of idea of what needed to be done.

John had returned to pick us up. I thanked them both and we left. Back at the hotel, I told Therezinha that on Friday we would go together to meet my friend, Aurea. Aurea and she could talk about California. Then I kissed her good night. She and John left.

Before I knew it, Friday arrived. The week was already gone! Nevertheless, my mission had been accomplished. Therezinha and I were going out that evening to meet Aurea, and I was looking forward to it. I hadn't been dancing in awhile.

Therezinha came to the hotel with Ana. We would meet Aurea in the hotel lobby. Aurea came in with her friend and introductions were made. Ana said that she knew of a popular disco in town. We took two cars. John drove Therezinha, Ana and me, and we would all come back with Aurea. We went into the club. The club had a beautiful view of the beaches and downtown Rio. It had a walkway around the outside of the building, and anyone could walk around it and view the entire city. I was impressed with the view. Inside, the club was nice and cozy. We sat down at a table and ordered some food and drinks. Therezinha sat next to Aurea, and they began to talk about California. Therezinha seemed to get excited about eventually living in California. Soon the music started, and we began to dance. The party continued until 2:00AM. Everyone had a great time.

Aurea took me back to my hotel, and I thanked her. Therezinha would be back early in the morning with John to pick me up and take me to the airport. They drove away. I packed my suitcase before I went to bed.

I felt as if I hadn't slept. John and Therezinha rang from the lobby, and I met them. We left for the airport. I kissed Therezinha goodbye. I would see her in July. We were getting married!!

Chapter
Nineteen

I had a lot to do in order to be ready to marry this summer, and I knew it.

Two weeks had gone by since I had returned from Brazil. I called Therezinha's cousin, Marcia, to see how everything was progressing in the family. Therezinha had to get some paperwork from the American Consulate in order to start the process. She was having problems acquiring some of the documents. I also had to receive some paperwork from them so that I could provide certain documents to the government of Brazil, which I didn't have on my person when I was there last. I knew that in order for the wedding to take place, I had to make it happen myself. This meant that I had to return to Brazil. There was no way around it. I told Marcia to let Therezinha know that I was returning to Brazil next month for a few days. I would have a lot to do in a short period of time, but I was determined to get it done while I was there.

Therezinha
Kevin came back in May to take care of the wedding. I was very happy
and sure of what I wanted. I was glad I hadn't accepted his proposal in
1992. It wasn't the right time. I wasn't prepared yet. The more I got to
know him, the more I knew. He did so many nice things for me, not in
the material sense but in a deeper sense. He really cared for me. To be
honest, I was never cared for in this way by any other man. He is a
different and wonderful person and I have no complaints.

I left for Los Angeles and then on to Brazil.

Therezinha was there waiting for me, along with her friend, Richard.
He drove the taxi. We left for the Ipanema Inn. I checked in and
had to rest. Therezinha said that Richard would be back in about
three hours, and we would go to her parents' house. Her mother had
been sick and I wanted to visit with her. Besides, I didn't have a
chance to see her father on my last visit. We had missed each other.

Richard and Therezinha left. After about two hours, I woke up,
showered, changed clothes and took a walk around the block. I
bought a shiny green plant for Therezinha's mother and then went
back to the hotel to wait for Richard. He was expected at 7:00PM.
He was right on time.

Therezinha's father was at the house this time. I greeted him, along
with her sisters and her brothers. Her mother was resting in the
bedroom. I gave her the plant. She liked it and was happy I was in
Brazil. Therezinha called Marcia. I wanted to get together with the
whole family and talk about the wedding. Marcia said that she would
come over to the family house on Wednesday, and we would discuss
everything. In the meantime, I would get the paperwork started at
the American Consulate. Marcia agreed with my tentative plans.

She said that would be good. Therezinha talked with her a little more after me. Ana had come over, and I asked her to tell Therezinha's father that I wanted to talk to him. I formally asked for Therezinha's hand in marriage. Ana translated what I said, and he gave me permission to marry his daughter. Therezinha was right there next to me. After awhile, Richard came and I said good night to everyone.

The next day, we had to go to the American Consulate together for the paperwork. Richard would pick me up at 10:00AM. I went next door for breakfast and returned to the hotel. Richard came with Ana and Therezinha.

When we arrived at the American Consulate, there was no one in the building, which was unusual. It was a holiday in the States. I had forgotten. Richard dropped us off and we walked around downtown. We didn't stay too long. Therezinha had to go back to help her mother around the house, and we decided that she and I would go shopping tomorrow for wedding clothes. We didn't have to be at the Consulate until 1:30PM, so we could do our shopping in the morning. Therezinha wanted me to buy my clothes in Brazil, since we were getting married there. You know the old saying, "When in 'Brazil' do like the 'Brazilians.'"

We caught another taxi back to the hotel and I said goodbye. I didn't do anything else that day, just walked around town a little, thinking.

I decided to call Claudio that evening to tell him I was back in town. He was happy to hear from me. He and Selma were doing fine. He understood that there was an awful lot to do in order to get married in Brazil, especially for an American. We talked for awhile, and I told him that I looked forward to seeing him in July.

Richard came to the hotel about 9:30 in the morning with Therezinha, and we drove to a mall. It was a huge place and had nice stores. Therezinha looked at dresses. I looked at pants and shirts. We shopped for awhile, looking and enjoying ourselves at the same time. We had to be at the Consulate at 1:30PM, so we had a quick lunch and Richard returned to take us back into the city. We went in. I got all of the paperwork and other documents that would be needed for Therezinha and I to be married. Also, the Consulate staff explained to me what they needed from us in the way of information. And it was a lot of information. All of the forms and documents had to be completed correctly upon submission in order for them to process our application. After we got the information, we left. My head spun with all the things we had to do in a very short period of time!

Therezinha had to go back to work. She was working part time. So we hailed two taxis, and we left in different directions. I would see her tomorrow at her parents' house. I read the information from the Consulate when I got back to the hotel. Now, I knew what had to be done, and it wasn't going to be all that easy. I went out in the evening for dinner, walked around for a little bit and returned to the hotel. The fresh air did me some good.

In the morning I began to work on some of the forms. I worked for awhile, and then Therezinha called. She said that Richard would be there at 7:00PM to pick me up and take me to her parents' house. Okay, I would be here. Everyone was at the house that evening. Marcia was there too. Most of the family watched TV as dinner was being prepared. Therezinha fixed me something to eat. Her mother looked much better and said that she was feeling better too. I was happy about that.

After my dinner, we all began to talk. Marcia translated. We set the wedding date and also discussed the location of the wedding and the reception. We decided that the reception would be at George and Rose Angela's, where Therezinha lived. After a few hours, we had taken care of most of the business of the wedding. Then a toast was announced, and all welcomed me into the family. I was glad to be a part of her family.

Marcia and I went on to discuss the paperwork from the American Consulate, and she explained it to Therezinha in Portuguese so that she would know exactly what to do. Tomorrow, Therezinha would do her paperwork. Richard returned to pick me up, and I said thank you to everyone and good night.

Well, everything started to take shape. There was still a lot to do, but every day a little more progress was made.

I knew that for the next couple of days Therezinha would be very busy getting her documents in order. She had to take different papers to different offices and have them reviewed and filed. Besides that, she had to work also. I knew that she was doing all she could to move the process along. She wanted this as much as I did.

Friday morning had arrived. The phone rang and I answered, "Hello."

It was Therezinha, she said to meet her at the Consulate at 1:00PM. She had some papers she wanted to turn in and wanted me to be there with her. After breakfast, I walked around for a bit, then got a taxi for downtown. I arrived a little early and waited for her. Ana arrived, and a little later Therezinha came, and we went inside the building. We turned in some papers she had completed, and I also got some clarity on the process, which I needed. After we finished talking to the Consulate staff, we left. The three of us caught a taxi back to Ipanema Beach and decided to have lunch at a little restaurant that Therezinha liked.

We walked around down by the beach and took some pictures. Therezinha had to take her mother to the doctor later in the day, so we decided not to go out that night. My flight was scheduled for early in the morning anyway.

We walked back to the hotel lobby, and Therezinha and Ana left.

I was glad I had come back! Otherwise, I was certain that the wedding would not have happened in July. Now, everything was on schedule, and it was just a matter of time before we would be married.

After dinner, I walked around Ipanema, until it started to rain. Then I returned to the hotel for the evening. I called Marcia and told her that I would stay in touch with her. I told her to let me know if Therezinha needed anything. Then we said goodbye until July.

I finished packing and fell asleep. The next morning came and I was well rested and ready to leave Brazil. Richard was waiting for me in the lobby. Therezinha and Ana were with him. We left for the airport.

I checked in and thanked Ana for all her help during the past week.

I kissed Therezinha goodbye. The next time I came back to Brazil, it would be to get married to Therezinha, which was a wonderful feeling. We had both been through so much over the years.

It was a smooth flight for the most part. It was Sunday when I got back to San Francisco, and I had a day to rest.

Everything was okay with the business. The next couple of weeks went by. Soon school would be out for the summer. I called Claudio to see how he and Selma were getting along. Claudio answered the phone. He told me that he had some bad news for me.

"What is it?"

He said that he wouldn't be able to be my best man, because of his job situation. His company was in the process of restructuring and he was about to be transferred to another part of Brazil. This meant that he was not permitted any time away. He couldn't leave town. He felt really bad about it. When he told me about this, I knew that he had to stay there and take care of business. It was his job.

I understood his position, and said hopefully, we would be able to see each other another time. Claudio said that he would call Therezinha and tell her the bad news. I knew she would be disappointed that he and Selma wouldn't be able to be at our wedding. After all, they were our good friends. We talked a little while longer and then said goodbye.

I thought to myself, 'Now, what else could happen?'

The wedding was going to take place. Nothing was going to stand in the way! Not this time!

Chapter
Twenty

July arrived, and I planned to go to Fort Lauderdale, Florida, for a family reunion. And from there, on to Brazil. So much had to be done in July regarding the business that I felt overwhelmed. All of the summer work had yet to be scheduled. Since I would be away for part of the summer, the regular schedules were of no use. In addition, several of the buses were due for state inspection. It had been a long seven and a half years, and I was ready to marry Therezinha. I planned to leave on Friday. On Wednesday, the California Highway Patrol had come to my place of business to inspect some of the buses. Just my luck! They found a problem with one of the buses, the best of the fleet, in fact. My mechanic came over the next day, Thursday, to fix the bus. Time was of the essence. I knew that I could not leave without the bus being fixed and inspected.

My sister-in-law, Cindy, and her new baby boy, Alvis III, and my nephew, Kyle, needed a ride to the San Francisco Airport. They were going to the family reunion also. I took them to the airport, dropped them off and sped back to my office. The mechanic said he had fixed the problem.

The California Highway Patrol came to re-inspect the bus. The same problem had occurred again. It was depressing. "Oh, no!"

I knew that my flight was scheduled to leave San Francisco early the next morning. The inspector said that he would meet me tomorrow to re-check the bus once again. This meant that I had to reschedule my flight. I was really depressed. I couldn't sleep that night. The next morning, I got up very early to get a head start on all of the things I had to do. Some clothes had to be washed, and a few items had to be picked up from the cleaners.

Around 9:00AM, the mechanic came and began to work on the bus again. He solved the problem this time! One hour later, the bus was fixed. I called the California Highway Patrol, they re-inspected and everything checked out. What a relief! I truly was leaving that night!

I made a checklist and began to check off the things that still needed to be done. Before I knew it, it was time to go to the airport. My flight to Florida was a night flight, so I could sleep on the plane. I took my seat and the only thoughts that came to me were about Therezinha. I was going be married to Therezinha! We would finally be together. Our honeymoon night... As the plane took off down the runway, I said to myself, 'Hearrrr we goooo!'

I arrived in Florida about 6:30AM on Saturday. My father met me at the airport along with my mother. They were happy to see me, and I told them about the bus and that I almost didn't make the reunion.

We left the airport for my grandmother's house. It was great to see her. At eighty-nine years of age, she was in very good shape. My grandmother was a very strong-minded woman, and I loved talking to her. We have had some very good conversations over the years. Conversations about everything.

The family planned a picnic in the park around noon. My brother Kirk stayed with one of my uncles next door to my grandmother's house. My father had built the duplex for his mother about ten years ago. It was a very nice property with a wide, flat backyard. My brother was happy to see me. We talked for a little while and then got ready to go to the picnic. It was hot, as usual. It was Florida. All my uncles and aunts were at the picnic, including all of the children, and all of their families. Our immediate family was at the reunion, with the exception of one of my sisters and her family. There was a lot of conversation, talking and laughing. My uncles fried fish, and chicken was grilled along with pork ribs. Huge bowls of beans, salad and pasta were placed on the tables. It was a real feast, and all types of drinks and desserts were there to be enjoyed after the barbecue.

The park was beautiful. Our tables were located on a lush, green lawn, and large and small trees filled the distance. Everyone talked and relaxed and shared. It's a natural part of any family reunion to find out what is going on with one another and offer advice to kin folks, especially if you felt they could benefit from it. Ours is a big family, and most everyone made it to the reunion. I had a great time with my family. But I couldn't stop thinking about the next part of my trip—it wouldn't be long now before I would be on my way to Brazil.

I stayed with my Uncle E.J. and Aunt Carmen. The family had arranged it that way, figuring that we had a lot to talk about.

Once at the house, I told Uncle E.J. that I was getting married to Therezinha, the woman from Brazil. He was a little surprised. He thought I would be marrying someone from the Dominican Republic. I explained to him that Therezinha and I had a history of ups and downs, but we were always understanding of one another, which was very important. He understood and wished me the best.

Later on that night, we went over to visit another of my uncles. His name is Otis and he is a preacher. We ate again and enjoyed talking with family members. About 10:30PM, we went back to Uncle E.J.'s. It was a long day, and the sun just seemed to draw energy out of me.

In the morning, my Aunt Carmen was up early, and she ironed my shirt for me. It was good to see her. She hadn't been at the picnic. She was as pretty and as kind to me as ever. We had breakfast and got ready for church.

Aunt Carmen's sister came over, and we all left for church. My uncle's church boasted more family members on that Sunday than the regular church members! When the ushers took up the collection, they brought in quite a bit more money than usual. My uncle was trying to raise enough money to remodel the church. Knowing my uncle, he would accomplish his goal.

After service, the family arranged a reunion banquet held at a fine restaurant. We were able to sit down together and talk about family matters and also plan for another reunion in a couple of years. The banquet was catered and the food was pretty good, but not as good as home-cooking. My immediate family planned to go to Disney World the next day. The next day was Monday.

My thoughts began to shift to Brazil again. After the banquet, my brothers and I went back to my grandmother's house, and we talked for awhile. Some more of the family members came to my grandmother's house, and we had a good time, as we kidded one another and laughed at the responses and retorts.

Uncle E.J. and I went back to his house. Aunt Carmen was up and we began to talk. She wanted to meet Therezinha, and I said, "You will, very shortly."

The next day, my Uncle Willie came over to Uncle E.J.'s around 8:00AM to pick me up for breakfast. Uncle Willie and I really get along fine and enjoy each other's company every time we are together. We had a nice big breakfast. Afterward, Uncle Willie had scheduled a mechanic to work on some of the church vans. It was another hot day in Florida, and I was ready to leave Fort Lauderdale. After the vans were fixed, my uncle and I went back to his house. Soon it was time to go to the airport. Uncle Willie had a meeting to attend, so I called my cousin Lisa and asked her to take me to the airport. Lisa and her mother Matty came to pick me up. I said goodbye to everyone and left.

I thanked them both for taking me. They wished me well. It had been an enjoyable family reunion. Everyone seemed to enjoy themselves, and I was glad that I was able to attend and be part of it. But now it was time for the best part of the trip, and that was to be on my way to see Therezinha.

The plane was filled with Brazilian students traveling back home. They were excited and talked loudly. I was excited myself. When the captain said we would be landing soon, I couldn't believe how fast the time went by!

The captain told us that we couldn't land right away because of fog at the Galiao Airport. We had to circle the airport until the fog cleared. I was anxious to get off the plane, but also realized he couldn't land unless he could see. I understand about "safety first," since I'm a school bus driver. After nearly an hour of circling, the fog had lifted enough for the captain to land the plane.

The landing was perfect. It was Tuesday morning. There were a lot of people waiting for the plane, since it had been delayed. I looked for Therezinha and couldn't see her. 'She must be late,' I thought. Every other time I had arrived in Rio de Janeiro, she had always been there to meet me. And after a long flight, it was always a pleasure to see her beautiful face and gorgeous smile. I sat around the airport for about ten minutes, waiting and watching people pass back and forth. Then I saw her and Ana walking toward me. Therezinha looked around for me, and when I called out her name, they came over. We kissed. Usually Therezinha took a taxi to the airport, but this time she had asked her friend to drive her and Ana.

Therezinha went off to find her friend, and Ana and I waited for her to return. About ten minutes later, she and her friend walked toward us. Therezinha introduced me to her friend Monica. We all left the airport together.

We were getting married in one week, and time flies in Rio, I've learned. So, after dropping off my bags at the Ipanema Inn, we went directly to the Intercontinental Rio Hotel in São Conrado. The hotel was located about ten minutes from Ipanema Beach. This would be the hotel where we would spend our honeymoon! When we drove up, we could see that the hotel was absolutely beautiful. We went inside to make reservations for our wedding day. The receptionist called a bellboy, and he showed us two rooms. I didn't like the first room, but the second room was very nice. Therezinha also liked the room. It was really beautiful. I wished that we were on our honeymoon at that very moment...

We went back down to the hotel lobby, walked around a little and then left the hotel. It was around lunch time and we were all hungry. Therezinha had a favorite little restaurant in Ipanema Beach that she liked, so we went there for lunch. And I was having fun at the restaurant, trying to learn as many Portuguese words as I could.

I needed to rest for awhile, so Therezinha said she would have her friend, Richard pick me up at 7:00PM. I said goodbye to Ana and Monica and thanked them for coming to meet me at the airport. I was exhausted. The sun was setting when I woke from my nap.

Richard, a really nice guy, was there promptly at 7:00PM. He told me that he had been to Fort Lauderdale once and remembered Sunrise Boulevard. We talked about the big flea markets on that stretch of highway.

About forty minutes later, we were at Therezinha's house. It was good to see her family again. Then she called Marcia. Marcia and I talked and decided that I would go over to her house on Thursday with Therezinha to check over the paperwork for the American Consulate. Then Therezinha could deliver all of the necessary documents. About an hour later, Richard came back. I said good night to the family and went back to the hotel.

The next day, Therezinha, Ana, Monica and I went shopping for our wedding clothes. We went to the Barra Shopping Center, which is one of the best shopping malls in the city. The mall serves an upscale clientele. People who shop at Barra have money, no doubt about it.

Around 10:30AM, Monica came and picked me up at my hotel, and she drove us to the shopping center. It was another beautiful winter day in Brazil. Personally, I liked the weather better in the winter. It was a little too hot for me in the summer there. Unlike California, even though it's winter, Brazil still maintains a tropical climate. To Brazilians, a California winter is very cold.

We walked in and out of several shops looking at different apparel. I had to buy a Brazilian shirt and pants to be married in to my Therezinha. It was an exciting feeling. Therezinha was very excited also, as she looked and looked, stopping at different shops and trying on different clothes. We walked by a man's shirt shop. I saw a nice blue-striped shirt. The material felt to be of good quality, and I decided to try it on. I requested the opinion of the three women with me, and they all agreed that it looked good, so I decided to buy it.

I thought to myself, 'Okay, I'm half way done with my outfit.'

We continued to walk around the huge mall. I saw a pair of blue slacks that looked almost like silk. We went into the store, and I tried on the slacks and another pair of pants. I wasn't quite sure of my pant size. One fit and one didn't. Both pairs had cuffs in them and needed to be let out a little. The store clerk said to come back in two hours. I was done with me! We men don't like to shop, so we pick out our clothes much faster than women.

After walking around the mall for about another hour, Therezinha still hadn't found anything that she had liked. We decided to sit down and have lunch at a restaurant inside the mall. Ana always helped me by translating the conversation and was very pleasant to be around. Monica was also very pleasant.

About an hour later, we began to walk around again. I wanted Therezinha to pick out a dress she really liked. After all, this was her wedding and she had to look beautiful. She shopped and shopped looking in different stores. She finally saw a dress that caught her eye, and she and Monica went into the store. I stayed outside in the mall area. I was sure that whatever she chose I would like. It was completely up to her. Finally, she decided on a dress that would be her wedding dress. After she purchased the dress, we decided to leave the mall. Whew! We had been there most of the day! But it was enjoyable, and we had accomplished what we had set out to do— buy our clothes for the wedding day, which was fast approaching.

There were still many more things to do. Back at the hotel, I thanked Ana and Monica for coming along and kissed Therezinha goodbye. As they drove away, I thought to myself, 'Wow, what a day! And tomorrow is already Thursday!'

Chapter
Twenty One

I woke around 9:00AM. I walked to my window and saw the beach crowded with *cariocas*. After breakfast I walked around Ipanema to get some exercise and work off some nervous energy. I didn't have much planned. Therezinha said she would call me around 5:00PM to tell me what time Richard would pick me up to take me to Marcia's house.

I decided to go down by the beach and watch the people go by and just enjoy the beautiful scenery, the water and mountains that encompass the Ipanema Beach. I was excited about finally marrying Therezinha. I came to believe that never in this lifetime would we be together—especially after she had said "No" to me in January of 1993. But when people are destined to be together, it happens, often in the most unpredictable ways.

I walked back to the hotel for the phone call. It was around 6:00PM, and Therezinha had not called me yet. An hour later, the phone rang.

"Hello."

It was Therezinha. She was downstairs in the lobby.

I said, "I'll be down in five minutes."

She had come in a taxi from work, and we got into the taxi to go to Marcia's house. It took about an hour to get there, with rush hour traffic still loading the highways. Marcia was fixing dinner and watching her child.

Therezinha had her paperwork with her. She had to take a physical for the Consulate to make sure that she was healthy enough to immigrate to the United States. I also took a test. Therezinha's sister Lucia had made our rings—a matching set of gold. Our rings were beautiful, and Therezinha had them engraved with our names and the wedding date. She showed Marcia and me the rings. Then Marcos came home, and we all sat down for dinner. Marcia had made chicken pot pie, rice, and a Brazilian salad, that I didn't care for too much. But the rest of the meal was very, very good. We also had flat beans, which were very tasty. Marcia is an excellent cook.

I felt comfortable with Marcia translating for me. This was a family matter, and she really tried her best to answer all of my questions and to explain to me the Brazilian wedding customs and culture. Marcia had explained again what Therezinha needed to do to complete the document process for the American Consulate. There were papers and forms still to be submitted to them in duplicate. We had all the information we needed, and now Therezinha knew exactly what to do. After we were married, I wouldn't be in Brazil with her, so it was very important that she knew what to do and how to do it— especially when responding to the American Consulate in Brazil.

We were originally scheduled to be married five days earlier in a little Catholic church with a priest presiding. But the date had to be changed because of the Brazilian government paperwork, and when the date was changed, the priest wasn't available. Also, the change in plans didn't allow Therezinha and me to have an extended honeymoon in Brazil.

We would have our honeymoon in the United States when she was able to get her visa. She understood and was okay with that.

It was around 10:00PM. Therezinha called a cab to come to get us. She was tired. She said she had been up early and had done a lot to get ready for the wedding, and she also had worked in the morning. I knew she had been doing a lot. I thanked Marcia and her husband for the dinner and for translating. We left in a cab. The driver dropped Therezinha off first. We said good night, with a kiss. She is so sweet to kiss!

Back at the hotel, I decided that I needed to unwind a bit and I ordered a coke at the hotel bar. I met a man who spoke English there named Leo. Leo was from Brazil, but he had traveled to New York, Los Angeles and San Francisco. He talked about the diamond business. We enjoyed the small talk and said good night to each other.

Finally, around 11:30PM, I went to my room. Time passed rapidly.

In the morning, I had remembered that Therezinha's younger sister Denise was having her birthday that day. I had nothing planned. Basically, I was just waiting for our wedding day. And of course, the wedding night! It was a cloudy day. It looked as if it could rain at any moment. The day dragged by slowly. Around 5:00PM, I was about to walk out of the lobby to get something to eat when one of the bellboys said that there was a phone call for me.

"Hello?"

It was Therezinha. She said that Richard would be there to pick me up at 7:00PM to take me to her house for Denise's birthday party. Richard came, and we left. We arrived around 8:00PM. I greeted her family and wished Denise a very happy birthday. There was food and drink, and everybody seemed to be having a good time. A special program about the National Basketball Association was on TV, and the program was in English. I enjoyed watching it with Therezinha's brother, brother-in-law and nephew. Denise's new baby girl Daniella was beautiful, and Therezinha watched her and enjoyed herself with Denise. Then I remembered that my friend Aurea had asked me to deliver some toys to her son. She had returned to the United States.

It was getting late. Therezinha called Richard to ask him to pick me up.

I thanked her family for inviting me to the party. I felt welcome, as always, at her parents' house. And considering her parents and I really couldn't talk to each other, we did try to make conversation as best we could. And that was fun.

I asked Therezinha to call Aurea's mother and schedule a meeting with her tomorrow in Niteroi. Richard would come by the hotel and pick me up around ten in the morning.

Richard came in the morning and we left. It was a nice day after the rain. The air seemed to be really fresh and clean. It was about a forty-five minute drive to Niteroi. When we arrived, Richard asked for directions to the street. It was a "walking" street only, so we had to park.

We got out and started to walk as we looked for the address. I delivered the toys to Aurea's mother, who was getting a haircut at the time. She thanked me, and Richard and I left. We walked down the street, and we saw people selling all kinds of items, a kind of two-sided flea market. There were a lot of things on display. You name it, they had it. I bought some Samba tapes—Brazilian music is very good, especially the Samba beat.

After looking around for awhile, we decided to go. We went back to Ipanema Beach. Richard left and said he would be back at 7:00PM to drive me to Therezinha's house. I couldn't wait to go to São Conrado and see some new scenery.

Richard arrived on time. Therezinha's sister Rose Angela and her husband George had just bought a new house. The house was really beautiful and so was the property. The backyard had a gentle, sloping hillside. They offered their house to us for our reception. I felt honored. In the rear patio area, there was a separate building, where Therezinha lives. Actually, it was her own little house. In order to get to Therezinha's house, you had to go through a gate, so it was a well-secured area. That evening a little street *junina*, or carnival, was arranged by the neighbors. There was food, games, music and dancing. They were raising money for the neighborhood. Everyone, from kids to adults, was having a good time. They even lit a small bon fire, and I watched it burn down. The kids popped firecrackers and bombs all night long, and the parents played bingo and gave out prizes. It was amazing how the neighbors had gotten together for a good cause.

Marcia and her parents came over, and Therezinha's parents were there as was most of her family. Marcia and I talked; it was enjoyable that she had come. Therezinha's older sister Rose Angela's birthday was the next day. They planned a party for Rose Angela and wanted me to come.

Marcia asked me, but I hadn't been feeling that well and I didn't want to get sick, especially away from home and, even more importantly, right before my marriage ceremony. I wanted to feel good all over, inside and out, on my wedding day. I told Marcia that I would call her in the morning and let her know if I was up to it.

Richard came at about 11:00PM to take me back to Ipanema Beach. I thanked the whole family for inviting me to their neighborhood carnival, and left.

I saw Leo again as I walked through the hotel lobby. We talked for a little while. He wanted to go out and have a drink, and asked me to join him. We walked to a pizza restaurant on the corner. We sat and talked for about an hour. By then I was really feeling ill. I should not have gone. The restaurant was stuffy, and some people were smoking. It began to affect my breathing, especially since I didn't feel well in the first place. Back to my room and to my bed.

I woke up feeling no better. I also had to move out of the hotel that day. The hotel expected a big group, and I was told on Tuesday when I checked in that I could have a reservation until Sunday only. I told the clerk that I would accommodate them.

I called Marcia around 10:00AM and told her that I was still feeling bad. The management relocated me next door to the Everest Park Hotel. That was fine with me; I had enjoyed staying there in December of 1992.

I checked in, went to the room and turned on the TV. The "Big Game" was being played today. Brazil and Uruguay were about to play for the soccer championship. I wanted to watch the football game. I knew that Brazil would probably win. I had never seen another team score on them. Their defense was awesome. Brazilians love their football. Brazil scored a goal in the first half, and that was normal. Uruguay didn't score. In the second half, Uruguay scored on a penalty kick, tying the game 1 to 1. I knew that it was a matter of time before Brazil would score again and win the game. But to my surprise, it didn't happen. The game went into overtime, and Uruguay won the game! The game was being played in Uruguay, and when Uruguay won, the crowds went crazy. They loved the fact that they had beaten Brazil, the best team in the world. It was a great game.

As I rested, I thought about the places I had been over the years. I was happy that I had given myself the opportunity to travel internationally. International travel exposed me to many different people and cultures. It changed me—the only way I can describe it is to say that it made me a "bigger" person. I will always have good memories of my travels, but the best thing that ever happened to me was having met Therezinha.

After the game, I went down to the hotel restaurant and ordered something to eat, hoping that I would feel better after dinner. No, I felt about the same. I decided to go outside for some fresh air, and take a short walk. I looked forward to leaving Ipanema Beach and going to São Conrado and staying at the Intercontinental Rio.

Chapter
Twenty Two

I felt much better by morning. I had a good breakfast of fruit, bread, juice, eggs and meats. I paid the bill and asked the bellboy to get me a taxi. It was 12:00PM. Then I exchanged some money and left the hotel to walk around Ipanema Beach one last time. The taxi pulled up and I was ready to leave.

I checked into the Intercontinental Rio. I was told that my room would be ready in an hour, so I walked around the hotel to familiarize myself. The place was incredible! On the grounds I saw a spa and an exercise room, two huge swimming pools, tennis courts and a small golf range. The beach was just across the street. When my room was ready, I walked through to see a cable TV with a satellite hook-up, a mini bar and a large balcony with a grand view of the beach. A luxurious king-size bed was placed in the center of the room.

I thought, 'Yeah, this bed would do "just fine!"'

I hadn't seen Therezinha since Saturday night. I wondered what she was thinking now that we were about to get married.

Therezinha
The wedding. To tell you the truth, I couldn't think clearly—my mind was going a thousand miles a minute. I was very nervous. The only thing I could say to my family was, "I am going to get married tomorrow!" For those seven and a half years, I never thought a relationship through the mail would lead me to City Hall. I say that because, in my entire life, I never saw myself married. I was very afraid of marriage. I had the fear that I was not going to find a good partner, friend… I was afraid that I was going to lose my freedom if I married. I was afraid that I was going to marry a jealous man who would jeopardize the relationship. When the day came, I prayed to God that everything would go well in my future, and I think He heard me. Kevin is a wonderful person, very understanding and a very good friend. He is everything. My life is going well, and I pray to God that it stays that way. With all those ups and downs during these seven and a half years, and everything that had happened in my life, it was worth it.

As I relaxed in the room, I clicked on the TV. With the cable hook-up, I got a few American channels. It was good to hear English spoken. The hotel seemed to offer everything. I could call Room Service if I got hungry day or night. So, I really didn't have to leave the room if I didn't want to. I thought about the wedding tomorrow. It would be a big day for me, and I would be married again. But this time it felt so right! Therezinha and I at last would make a commitment to bring our lives together "forever."

I finally got tired of watching movies and went down to the lobby and walked around a little more. I passed by a little restaurant and ordered some Brazilian chicken soup. It was really good and very filling.

After dinner, I walked around the hotel a little more, and then headed back to my room to get ready for bed. I wanted to be well-rested for the biggest day of my life.

Marcia called me with directions to the Civil Building, the location of the ceremony. She asked how I was feeling.

"Much, much better, Marcia."

I turned in early, put my head to the pillow, and in a moment I was asleep.

The sun was shining early in the morning. I expected a very hot day. How lucky we were to be getting married on such a beautiful day!

I was ready to get married. Breakfast was served by the pool. I started to get a little nervous, which was unusual for me. I went back to the room, laid out my clothes and called the lobby to arrange for a taxi. I needed the taxi to be at the hotel at 12:30PM for the drive to the Civil Building. Time now seemed to fly.

Before I knew it, it was time to go. The driver was waiting in front of the hotel, and away we went! I gave him the directions. He followed the directions, but it was not the right place!

"Oh no! What am I going to do?"

I started to get nervous, and it was also very hot in the taxi. The driver could speak a little English, and I mentioned the Civil Building to him. And he knew what I was talking about because he had gotten married there himself.

"All right!"

It was about 1:05PM. He said that we would be there in about five minutes. The traffic was light heading into the city.

When we drove up, I heard someone call out my name. I looked up and saw everyone waiting. We started up a steep staircase and everyone walked slowly so that they could keep their balance.

Therezinha looked beautiful in the dress she had picked out. Her face glowed, and she looked very happy. Most of her family was there with us, and it was really good to see them. After a few minutes, Therezinha and I and Monica and her brother-in-law George went into the room and signed papers for the marriage certificate. This took about fifteen minutes. Then we went back out to the lobby.

There were a lot of people waiting to get married today, and it was hot inside the building. A large fan was operating, but it wasn't enough to keep the lobby cool. Finally, we all went into the judge's chambers, a small little chamber. The judge began with a prayer, I believe, after all, I don't speak Portuguese. There were three other couples before us. We were to be married last. We had more family members than the other two couples, which was great.

The first ceremony went really fast. Therezinha's family began to take pictures of us, and our excitement kept heightening. Anyone there could really feel the excitement in the judge's chambers. I was even more nervous now, but I looked at Therezinha and said to myself, 'She is beautiful and she is mine!'

We were the next couple to be married. We were called forth to face the judge. She seemed very nice. She stepped up and spoke a few words, then grabbed our hands together and blessed us. After the blessing, I put Therezinha's ring on her finger, and she put my ring on my finger. Then we kissed. The family congratulated us, and we went back out to the lobby.

Therezinha had the wedding certificate, and we went upstairs to an office to file the certificate with the government in Rio. The office would then send it to the American Consulate, so that when Therezinha went there for her visa, all the paperwork would be in place for her. It was a nice ceremony, even though it went very fast. After filing the paperwork, we went back outside to catch a taxi to the Intercontinental Rio Hotel. The reception would start around 7:00PM. We said goodbye to the family and caught a cab.

On the way back to the hotel, I thought, 'It is finally over. Therezinha is now my wife.' I would look over at her and just smile. She seemed to be very happy too. I really hadn't seen her this happy before, except that first night we met. I remember that night as if it were yesterday. But it wasn't! So much had happened in between for both of us, but I do remember her beautiful face that night, and I saw that she was happy that we met. I lost myself in my thoughts for most of the drive. We came up to the hotel. It was now mid-day. We held each other's hand and walked into the hotel together. I felt like a king with my queen. She made me feel proud to be with her. And she was excited too—I could see it in her face.

"Let's go to the room and settle in, then walk around the hotel," I said to her.

We went upstairs to our room and went in. She seemed to like the room very much; her eyes moved toward the French doors that opened onto the balcony. She slowly opened the doors and walked out to see the view of São Conrado and its white, glistening beaches stretching alongside the blue-green waters of the South Atlantic Ocean. The sun shone down on her and the beautiful country that was Brazil. After a few minutes, Therezinha came back into the room and opened her suitcase and put some clothes into dresser drawers and hung up a few things. Then we went out and walked through the hotel. I showed her the pools and the tennis court, the exercise room and the sauna, the restaurant—everything. We browsed in some shops and enjoyed the gentle, romantic ambiance. We decided to have lunch at the hotel's restaurant rather than leave. After the buffet service, we walked to the bar and had drinks. I ordered two cokes.

With gentle expressions, we began to talk. Even though we didn't speak the other's language fluently, Therezinha could somewhat understand me when I talked to her, and I could somewhat understand her when she spoke in Portuguese. But the effort was the best part, being together, alone, with no translator. It was great. We didn't want anyone else to be there. It was finally "our" time.

Therezinha seemed quite comfortable at the hotel. The atmosphere was relaxing and expansive. I told her that people come to her country and stay in places like this hotel all of the time. They swim in the pools, play golf on the ranges, play tennis on the courts, sit in the saunas, exercise in the weight rooms, dance at the discos, eat at fine restaurants and enjoy themselves every day of the year in her country. And I wanted to expose her to this way of living and to tell her at the same time that she deserves this kind of comfort and beauty, and that I'm going to do my best for her.

After our drinks, we decided to go back up to our room for awhile. It was now about 5:00PM, two hours before we were to leave for our reception. I sat down and turned on the TV. I found a newspaper in

English, *USA Today*. I began to read the paper, but I couldn't comprehend a word I was reading. Therezinha was there, sitting on the bed, and my mind was strictly on her. She looked so good! I wanted to just jump on top of her right then!

Therezinha asked if we could call Claudio and Selma. Selma was home by now. She told Therezinha that he would call us later on that evening, once we had returned from the reception.

We both went out onto the balcony and looked down at the beaches and the sea below. What a sight! I stood behind her with my arms around her. She felt so warm and soft. I just wanted to squeeze her body next to mine and hold her there with me.

To the left of the hotel, atop Corcovado Mountain, was the statute of Christ the Redeemer. I remembered how it was aglow at night, giving light to the city…

After awhile, we left the balcony. The TV was on already, and we sat on the bed to watch. A movie had just started. The movie was about a possessed car that wreaked havoc on it enemies. It was in English with Portuguese sub-titles, which was great for us. Therezinha listened to the words in English, and I read the Portuguese sub-titles. Then we compared words. It was fun, and we struggled with words foreign to both of us throughout the movie.

Richard rang our room. We quickly freshened up and left the hotel for the reception. It took about an hour to get to Rose Angela's. We were greeted by her family, all of whom threw rice at us as we walked in. It was great. Once inside, our guests greeted us one by one, while others talked and laughed as they celebrated our marriage. Everyone was in good spirits. Plenty of food and drink was put out for the guests to take as they wished. Marcia was busy video-taping the reception. I would have the video to show my family and friends our wedding night party and how much fun we had in Brazil.

Even Marcia's sister was there, along with her husband. I had met them both briefly in December of 1992 at Therezinha's parents' home. I remembered Maria Jose and Anael to have been very friendly and warm. Anael had been to New York several times and he spoke English quite well. Many others, including Therezinha's aunts and uncles, cousins, nieces and nephews, brothers, sisters and friends from work—everybody was there to celebrate with us. I felt welcomed into the family.

Therezinha mingled with the guests and chatted with her family and friends. She looked very happy, and it showed. Everyone could tell that we were both exhilarated by the wedding and the celebration.

The time had come to cut the wedding cake, a beautiful white coconut cake. I had brought a card to give to Therezinha. It was a poem, and for myself, it described our love and our enduring relationship. I asked Marcia to translate the poem for me, and she said that she would. So, after the cake-cutting, it was time to read the poem. I began to read it, and Marcia translated in Portuguese. It wasn't a long poem, but it was very romantic. When I finished, everyone burst into applause. A song had begun that told of blessings for us and our marriage. The entire celebration was a tremendously emotional experience for me. Therezinha's family was so close and loving with one another that I could literally see and feel this love everywhere around me.

The eating, drinking, singing and dancing continued. I pulled back a bit; I wanted the evening to be Therezinha's. I had had my first marriage. She had never been married before, and I wanted her family and friends to share with her and experience her happiness. She deserved to be happy. She had been waiting a long time for happiness—not that she had been waiting for me, but that she had been reluctant until that "special" someone came into her life—and it just happened to be me!

It was well after midnight, and the guests began to leave. Almost everyone had to go to work the next day. Each guest came up to us and kissed Therezinha and me goodbye. Ana came up to me and said a special congratulations, and I said, "Thank you, Ana. I've known you as long as I've known Therezinha." I was glad that she could be a part of our happiness. After all, it was her translating efforts that had helped me out that first night in Monte Libano.

Therezinha called Richard to come to get us. His taxi came and we said our goodbyes to everybody and thanked them for the wonderful reception they gave to us. I really enjoyed the warm and loving atmosphere as so many people wished us the best on our wedding day.

It felt funny to have Therezinha with me in the taxi. For so many years I had always said good night to her and left for a hotel room alone. But tonight she was mine!

When we got to the hotel, a message waited for us. Claudio had called and asked that we call him. He wanted to congratulate us on our marriage. I called him and Therezinha spoke with him and then gave me the phone. We talked about the day and how much he was missed among the guests. Then we said good night.

I decided to call my mother. She hadn't heard from me in a week. I knew that she would be worrying about her oldest son, not that there was anything to worry about, but that's how mothers are…

Therezinha looked so good sitting next to me on the side of the bed with her pajamas. Anyway, I managed to keep calm and call my mother. She was okay and she wanted to know about the wedding and the reception. I told her about the day. Then she wanted to say hello to Therezinha. I gave the phone to Therezinha.

She said, "Hello, how are you?"

She understood some of my mother's conversation. Therezinha said that she enjoyed talking to my mother and looked forward to meeting her and the rest of my family when she arrived in California.

It was now time to go to bed with the woman that I always dreamed of having.

When I came out of the bathroom, Therezinha was in the bed. The next thing I knew, we were kissing each other passionately. Physically, I was tired. It had been a very long day with huge emotions coming and going throughout the day. Mentally, after seven and a half years of fantasizing about being with her, my mind raced a thousand miles a minute. I slipped my hands over her beautiful, firm breasts and began to caress them. Just the touch of them drove me "wild" inside.

Therezinha moaned ever so lightly, and I could feel her heartbeat. It was beating with anticipation. I slipped off her pajama bottoms and panties and removed my pajamas and shorts and just looked at her whole body. Therezinha has nice, big, firm, round thighs and beautiful legs. I called them "bedroom legs." They were "gorgeous!!" Just looking at her excited me. We made passionate love to one another. After our love-making, we fell asleep and woke around six in the morning. I took a shower and got back into bed. I had to leave Therezinha that day. I hadn't gotten enough of her. But I knew that I had to discipline my mind again in order to be away from her for a period of time. I didn't know when she would be granted a visa. I didn't know what day she would come to me in California. I looked at her while she slept and didn't want to wake her. I just looked at her and smiled.

After awhile, Therezinha woke up. She said she had a headache. She drank a little too much champagne. Therezinha is not a drinker. Neither am I. She took some aspirin, then got up and took a shower. We got dressed and went to the hotel restaurant to have breakfast.

We ordered a large meal, both of us were hungry, and just looked at each other and smiled. Inside I was sad because I had to return home without my wife.

After breakfast, we went to the poolside. Therezinha took off her shorts and her top. She had on a bikini. Wow! I had been waiting to see her in a bikini. All of the other times I had visited her in Brazil, I had never seen her in a bikini—and it was worth the wait. She was beautiful from top to bottom!!

We sat down on some chairs at the poolside and took in the warmth of the morning sun. It was hot. Therezinha jumped in the pool to cool off. She looked beautiful. I loved seeing her when her hair was wet. It was straight, black and silky. We relaxed for about two hours, and then we headed back to the room to get ready to check out. We had some last-minute errands to take care of before my trip. Back in the room, Therezinha showered and I packed my suitcase. We took some pictures of the hotel room and the view of the beach, and then we went downstairs to check out.

Richard came for us and we left. It was too short a stay at the Intercontinental Rio, but the time we spent was just great. We drove into the city and took care of some details regarding Therezinha's travel plans, and then we went to her parents' house. Marcia had already made a tape of the reception, and we sat down and watched it with her family. The video came out pretty good, and I enjoyed seeing it before I left. Therezinha would bring me a copy when she came to California. Her mother cooked a delicious meal for us. Therezinha and I ate in the kitchen and talked. There were still some more forms that needed to be filled out for the American Consulate, so I did the paperwork. Marcia called to say goodbye. I thanked her for everything, and I said that I would call her and keep in touch. Marcia assured me that Therezinha would let her know if she needed anything from me.

It was time to leave. Ana dropped by to show me some jewelry she had recently made. I bought a few pieces from her. I thanked Therezinha's parents and the rest of her family, and we left for the airport. Therezinha's sister Denise and her friend came along, and so did Ana. Off we went to the airport.

I kissed Therezinha goodbye and went to board the plane. Once past Customs, I looked back and saw her looking at me. I blew her a kiss. She smiled and waved. Her face looked sad. But we both knew that soon she would be with me in San Francisco. We were about to begin our new life together in America!

Acknowledgements

From the first words written to the final manuscript that went to publication, four years were spent where I had to make things happen on my own. These efforts were supported by many individuals who provided me with personal and professional help along the way, and I am indebted to them. Author Leslie A.P. Esdaile for giving me the encouragement to write this book. Her thoughtful conversations inspired me. Author Douglas Childress for his publishing advice. Carolyn Waskom and Leona Jamison for helping me prepare the manuscript. My editor, Sherry K. Brennan, for her honesty, support and expertise. And I truly wish to thank my family and friends who believe in me and my dreams. Most of all, I want to thank Therezinha for her support during the course of this work.

This book was written for your reading enjoyment.

That which is truly worthwhile requires time and effort.
—Abigail Van Buren

Therezinha
By Kevin Allen
ISBN: 0-9671490-0-2

Available at your local bookstore or use this page to order.

☐ Therezinha $19.95/$23.95 Canada   Number of copies ———
Send to: One Lighthouse Press, 22 Dutton Court, Marin City, CA 94965

Please send me the items I have checked above. I am enclosing $ ———
Please add $3 per book to cover postage and handling. Send check or money order.
No cash or C.O.D.'s please.

Mr./Mrs./Ms. ————————————
Address ————————————

City/State ———————————— Zip ———

Please allow four to six weeks for delivery. Prices and availability subject to change without notice.